RevisionGuide

GCSEChemistry

Sam Goodman and Chris Sunley

Series editor: Jayne de Courcy

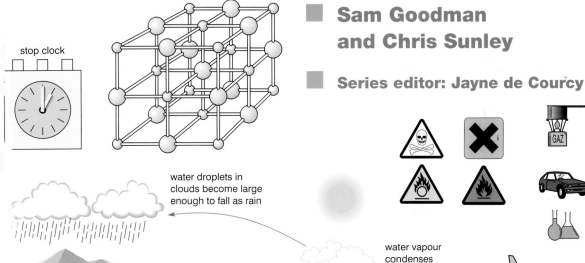

stop clock

water droplets in clouds become large enough to fall as rain

water vapour condenses to form clouds

water evaporates

rivers and streams flow back to the sea

CONTENTS AND REVISION PLANNER

ABOUT THIS BOOK

Exams are about much more than just repeating memorised facts, so we have planned this book to make your revision as active and effective as possible.

How?

- by breaking down the content into manageable chunks (Revision Sessions)

- by testing your understanding at every step of the way (Check Yourself Questions)

- by providing extra information to help you aim for the very top grade (A* Extras)

- by highlighting Ideas and Evidence topics (Ideas and Evidence)

- by listing the most likely exam questions for each topic (Question Spotters)

- by giving you invaluable examiner's guidance about exam technique (Exam Practice)

REVISION SESSION I

Revision Sessions

- Each Unit is divided into a number of **short revision sessions**. You should be able to read through each of these in no more than 30 minutes. That is the maximum amount of time that you should spend on revising without taking a short break.

- Ask your teacher for a copy of your own exam board's **GCSE Chemistry specification**. Match the topics in it with this book's Contents list, ticking off in the box headed '**On specification**' each of the revision sessions that you need to cover. It will probably be most of them.

CHECK YOURSELF QUESTIONS

- At the end of each revision session there are some **Check Yourself Questions**. By trying these questions, you will immediately find out whether you have understood and remembered what you have read in the revision session. **Answers** are at the back of the book, along with **extra hints and guidance**.

- If you manage to give correct answers to all the Check Yourself questions for a session, then you can confidently tick off this topic in the box headed '**Revised & understood**'. If not, you will need to tick the '**Revise again**' box to remind yourself to return to this topic later in your revision programme.

A* EXTRA

These boxes occur in each revision session. They contain some **extra information** which you need to learn if you are aiming to achieve the very top grade. If you have the chance to use these additional facts in your exam, it could make the difference between a good answer and a very good answer.

IDEAS AND EVIDENCE

Chemistry GCSE specifications have **particular topics highlighted** as 'ideas and evidence'. Every Foundation and Higher Tier paper must have at least one question on one of these topics.

The boxes in the book highlight the sort of questions you may meet in relation to themes such as the development of chemical ideas, the applications of chemistry, environmental issues and economic factors.

QUESTION SPOTTER

It's obviously important to revise the facts, but it's also helpful to know **how you might need to use this information** in your exam.

The authors, who have been involved with examining for many years, know the sorts of questions that are most likely to be asked on each topic. They have put together these Question Spotter boxes so that they can help you to **focus your revision**.

Exam Practice

- This Unit gives you **invaluable guidance on how to answer exam questions well**.

- It contains some sample students' answers to typical exam questions, followed by examiner's comments on them, showing where the students gained and lost marks. Reading through these will help you get a very clear idea of what you need to do in order to score **full marks** when answering questions in your GCSE Chemistry exam.

- There are also some **typical exam questions** for you to try answering. Model answers are given at the back of the book for you to check your own answers against. There are also examiner's comments, highlighting **how to achieve full marks**.

About your GCSE Chemistry course

Does this book match my course?

This book has been written to support all the single-award Chemistry GCSE specifications, including modular specifications, produced by the four examining groups in England and Wales. These specifications are based on the National Curriculum Key Stage 4 Programmes of Study. This means that although different specifications may group and arrange the content in different ways, they must all cover the same work. Ask your teacher for a copy of the specification you are following so that you can use it as a check-list.

Foundation and Higher Tier papers

In your GCSE Chemistry exam you will be entered for either the Foundation Tier exam papers or the Higher Tier exam papers. The Foundation exams allow you to obtain grades from G to C. The Higher exams allow you to obtain grades from D to A*.

	Higher Tier						
A*	A	B	C	D	E	F	G
			Foundation Tier				

What will my exam questions be like?

The exam questions will be of a type known as structured questions. Usually these are based on a particular topic and will include related questions. Some of these questions will require short answers involving a single word, phrase or sentence. Other questions will require a longer answer involving extended prose. You will have plenty of practice at both types of questions as you work through this book.

Short answer questions

These are used to test a wide range of knowledge and understanding quite quickly. They are often worth one mark each.

Extended prose questions

These are used to test how well you can link different ideas together. Usually they ask you to explain ideas in some detail. It is important to use the correct scientific terms and to write clearly. They may be worth four or five marks, and sometimes more.

Ideas and Evidence questions

How scientific ideas grow, and how they are communicated, will form part of your exam. Often this means that quite a lot of information is given in the question. *Don't panic over such questions* – you may not be familiar with the particular example in the question, but the point is that a number of themes apply to scientific development in general. Use the Ideas and Evidence boxes in this book to see examples of these themes.

Quality of written communication

There will be marks for this in your exam. Remember to use capital letters at the start of sentences and full stops at the end. Check your spelling carefully, and try to use the correct technical words where you can.

How should I answer exam questions?

- Look at the *number of marks*. The marks should tell you how long to spend on a question. A rough guide is a minute for every mark. The number of marks will indicate how many different points are required in the answer.
- Look at the *space allocated for the answer*. If only one line is given, then only a short answer is required, e.g. a single word, a short phrase or a short sentence. Some questions will require more extended writing and for these four or more lines will be allocated.
- *Read the question carefully*. Students frequently answer the question they would like to answer, rather than the one that has actually been set! Circle or underline the key words. Make sure you know what you are being asked to do. Are you choosing from a list? Are you using the periodic table? Are you completing a table? Have you been given the formula you will need to use in a calculation? Are you describing or explaining?

UNIT 1: ATOMIC STRUCTURE, BONDING AND PROPERTIES

REVISION SESSION 1 ▬ Ideas about atoms and their structure

⌗ How did the model of the atom evolve?

- The Ancient Greek thinker Democritus first suggested the idea of atoms around 2500 years ago. He said everything in the universe was made up of tiny **indivisible particles.** ('Indivisible' means 'cannot be split up into anything smaller'.) He called these particles **atoms**.

- Democritus's theory of atoms was not accepted then, because people refused to accept something that they could not see. The idea of 'atoms' was not raised again for over 2000 years.

- In 1808, the British chemist **John Dalton** published a book outlining his **theory of atoms**. These were the main points of his theory:

  1 All matter is made of small, indivisible spheres called atoms.
  2 All the atoms of a given **element** are identical and have the **same mass**.
  3 The atoms of **different elements** have **different masses**.
  4 Chemical **compounds** are formed when **atoms join together**.
  5 All molecules of a chemical compound have the **same type** and **number** of atoms.

- By the late 1800s, most scientists accepted Dalton's theory of atoms because it explained the results of their experiments on elements and compounds.

- Two suggestions in Dalton's theory were later proved wrong. Firstly, atoms are **divisible**, since they are made of even smaller, **sub-atomic particles** called protons, neutrons and electrons. Secondly, the atoms of an element may have different numbers of neutrons, and so have very slightly different masses. These atoms of different mass are called isotopes of the element (see page 4).

- The model of the atom we accept today is Dalton's basic model, revised when sub-atomic particles and isotopes were discovered.

(see page 4)

⚡ A* EXTRA

- If there is more than one line for your answer to a question on Dalton's atomic theory, you are expected to give an 'extended writing' answer.
- Often this is where you could get an extra mark for the use of 'correct' English, ideas in the correct order, and correct use of scientific terms. Dalton's theory is a good opportunity for you to practise this kind of 'extended writing' answer.

💡 QUESTION SPOTTER

- Questions will expect you to list the basic ideas of Dalton's atomic theory *and* to say which ones are still relevant today.
- You will need to remember the main points of the theory and point out that atoms are 'divisible' (into electrons, protons and neutrons) and that masses of the atoms of the same element can be different (isotopes).

✦ IDEAS AND EVIDENCE

The modern model of the atom came from experiments done by English scientists:
▸ In 1897, J.J. Thompson showed that negative particles – **electrons** – are present in all elements. Atoms are neutral, so they must also have a positive part – containing protons.
▸ In 1911, Ernest Rutherford showed that the atom has a positive central part – the **nucleus**. Electrons move round the nucleus like the planets round the Sun.
▸ In 1932, James Chadwick showed that the nucleus has another type of particle in it. This particle has the same mass as the proton, but no charge. It was named the **neutron**.

CHECK YOURSELF QUESTIONS

Q1 Democritus put forward his idea of atoms about 2500 years ago. Why did other Ancient Greeks not accept this idea?

Q2 State three of Dalton's ideas in his theory of atoms.

Q3 State two ideas that Dalton had about atoms that were later found to be incorrect. Why are they incorrect?

Answers are on page 155.

How are atoms put together?

Sub-atomic articles

■ The smallest amount of an element that still behaves like that element is an **atom**. Each element has its own unique type of atom. Atoms are made up of smaller, sub-atomic particles. The three main sub-atomic particles are: **protons**, **neutrons** and **electrons**.

■ These particles are very small and have very little mass. However, it is possible to compare their masses using a **relative scale**. Their charges can also be compared in a similar way. The proton and neutron have the **same** mass, and the proton and electron have **opposite** charges.

Sub-atomic particle	Relative mass	Relative charge
proton	1	+1
neutron	1	0
electron	$\frac{1}{2000}$	−1

■ Protons and neutrons are found in the centre of the atom, in a cluster called the **nucleus**. The electrons form a series of 'shells' around the nucleus.

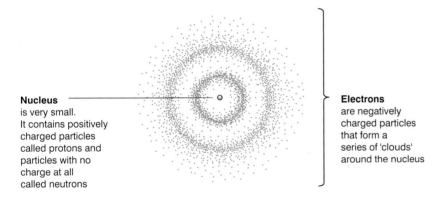

Nucleus
is very small.
It contains positively
charged particles
called protons and
particles with no
charge at all
called neutrons

Electrons
are negatively
charged particles
that form a
series of 'clouds'
around the nucleus

What are atomic number and mass number?

■ In order to describe the numbers of protons, neutrons and electrons in an atom, scientists use two numbers. These are called the **atomic number** and the **mass number**.

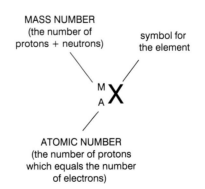

MASS NUMBER
(the number of
protons + neutrons)

symbol for
the element

$_A^M X$

ATOMIC NUMBER
(the number of protons
which equals the number
of electrons)

- The atomic number is used to order the elements in the periodic table. The atomic structures of the first ten elements are shown here.

Element	Atomic number	Mass number	Number of protons	Number of neutrons	Number of electrons
Hydrogen	1	1	1	0	1
Helium	2	4	2	2	2
Lithium	3	7	3	4	3
Beryllium	4	9	4	5	4
Boron	5	10	5	5	5
Carbon	6	12	6	6	6
Nitrogen	7	14	7	7	7
Oxygen	8	16	8	8	8
Fluorine	9	19	9	10	9
Neon	10	20	10	10	10

- **Hydrogen** is the only atom that has **no neutrons**.

Isotopes

- Atoms of the same element with the **same number** of protons and electrons but **different** numbers of neutrons are called **isotopes**. For example, there are three isotopes of hydrogen:

Isotope	Symbol	Number of neutrons
normal hydrogen	^1_1H	0
deuterium	^2_1H	1
tritium	^3_1H	2

- Isotopes have the same chemical properties but slightly different physical properties.

How are electrons arranged in the atom?

- The electrons are arranged in **shells** around the nucleus. The shells do not all contain the same number of electrons – the shell nearest to the nucleus can only take two electrons, whereas the next one further from the nucleus can take eight.

- Oxygen has an atomic number of 8, so has 8 electrons. Of these, 2 will be in the first shell and 6 will be in the second shell. This arrangement is written 2, 6. A phosphorus atom with an atomic number of 15 has 15 electrons, arranged 2, 8, 5.

Electron shell	Maximum number of electrons
1	2
2	8
3	8

- The electron arrangements are very important as they determine the way that the atom reacts chemically.

⊡ Atom diagrams

■ The atomic structure of an atom can be shown simply in a diagram.

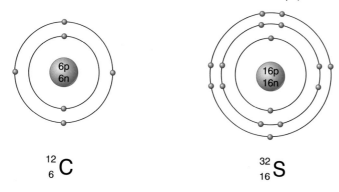

$$^{12}_{6}C \qquad ^{32}_{16}S$$

Atom diagrams for carbon and sulphur showing the number of protons and neutrons, and the electron arrangements.

? CHECK YOURSELF QUESTIONS

Q1 Explain the meanings of:
  a atomic number
  b mass number.

Q2 Copy out and then complete the table.

Atom	Number of protons	Number of neutrons	Number of electrons	Electron arrangement
$^{28}_{14}Si$				
$^{26}_{12}Mg$				
$^{32}_{16}S$				
$^{40}_{18}Ar$				

Q3 The table below shows information about the structure of six particles (A–F).

  a In each of the questions **i** to **v**, choose one of the six particles A–F. Each letter may be used once, more than once or not at all.
  Choose a particle that:
   i has a mass number of 12
   ii has the highest mass number
   iii has no overall charge
   iv has an overall positive charge
   v is the same element as particle E.

Particle	Protons (positive charge)	Neutrons (neutral)	Electrons (negative charge)
A	8	8	10
B	12	12	10
C	6	6	6
D	8	10	10
E	6	8	6
F	11	12	11

  b Draw an atom diagram for particle F.

Answers are on page 155.

Chemical bonding

⌘ How do atoms combine?

- Atoms bond together with other atoms in a chemical reaction to make a compound. For example, sodium will react with chlorine to make sodium chloride; hydrogen will react with oxygen to make water.

- This reactivity is due to the electron arrangements in atoms. If atoms have **incomplete electron shells** they will usually react with other atoms. Only atoms with complete electron shells tend to be unreactive. The **noble gases**, atoms in group 8 (sometimes referred to as group 0) of the periodic table, fall into this category.

- When atoms combine they try to achieve **full outer electron shells**. They do this either by gaining electrons to fill the gaps in the outer shell or by losing electrons from the outer shell to leave an inner complete shell.

- There are two different ways in which atoms can bond together: **ionic** bonding and **covalent** bonding.

⌘ What happens in ionic bonding?

- Ionic bonding involves **electron transfer** between metals and non-metals. Both metals and non-metals try to achieve complete outer electron shells.

- **Metals lose electrons** from their outer shells and form **positive** ions. This is an example of **oxidation**.

- **Non-metals gain electrons** into their outer shells and form **negative** ions. This is an example of **reduction**.

- The ions are held together by strong electrical (electrostatic) forces.

- The bonding process can be represented in **dot-and-cross diagrams**. Look at the reaction between sodium and chlorine as an example.

⚡ A* EXTRA

▶ When atoms form ions they try to complete their outer electron shell. For metals to do this it is easier to lose electrons than to gain them. For non-metals it is easier to gain electrons than to lose them. The number of electrons that need to be lost or gained is equal to the group number in the periodic table.

Sodium is a metal. It has an atomic number of 11 and so has 11 electrons, arranged 2, 8, 1. Its atom diagram looks like this:

Chlorine is a non-metal. It has an atomic number of 17 and so has 17 electrons, arranged 2, 8, 7. Its atom diagram looks like this:

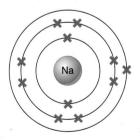

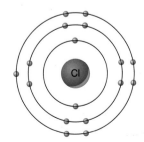

Sodium has one electron in its outer shell. It can achieve a full outer shell by losing this electron. The sodium atom transfers its outermost electron to the chlorine atom.

Chlorine has seven electrons in its outer shell. It can achieve a full outer shell by gaining an extra electron. The chlorine atom accepts an electron from the sodium.

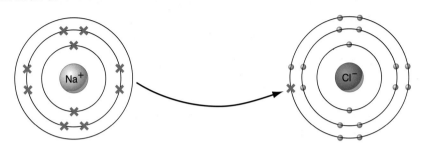

The sodium is no longer an atom; it is now an ion. It does not have equal numbers of protons and electrons, it is no longer neutral. It has one more proton than it has electrons, so it is a positive ion with a charge of 1+. The ion is written as Na^+.

The chlorine is no longer an atom; it is now an ion. It does not have equal numbers of protons and electrons, it is no longer neutral. It has one more electron than protons, so it is a negative ion with a charge of 1–. The ion is written as Cl^-.

METALS CAN TRANSFER MORE THAN ONE ELECTRON TO A NON-METAL

■ Magnesium combines with oxygen to form **magnesium oxide**. The magnesium (electron arrangement 2, 8, 2) transfers two electrons to the oxygen (electron arrangement 2, 6). Magnesium therefore forms a Mg^{2+} ion and oxygen forms an O^{2-} ion.

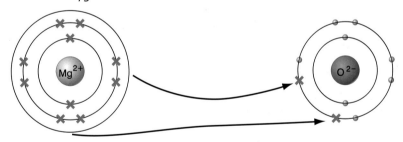

Dot and cross diagram for magnesium oxide, MgO

■ Aluminium has an electron arrangement 2, 8, 3. When it combines with fluorine with an electron arrangement 2, 7, three fluorine atoms are needed for each aluminium atom. The formula of **aluminium fluoride** is therefore AlF_3.

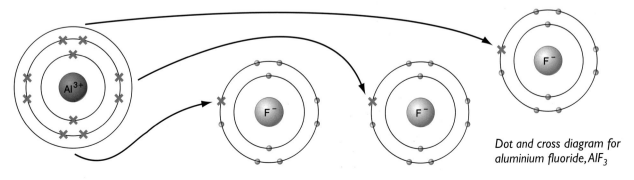

Dot and cross diagram for aluminium fluoride, AlF_3

What ions can an element form?

- The ion formed by an element can be worked out from the **position of the element in the periodic table**. The elements in group 4 and group 8 (or 0) generally do not form ions.

Group number	1	2	3	4	5	6	7	8 (or 0)
Ion charge	1+	2+	3+	X	3−	2−	1−	X

What is covalent bonding?

- Covalent bonding involves electron sharing. It occurs between atoms of non-metals. It results in the formation of a **molecule**. The non-metal atoms try to achieve complete outer electron shells.

- A **single covalent bond** is formed when two atoms each contribute one electron to a **shared pair** of electrons. For example, hydrogen gas exists as an H_2 molecule. Each hydrogen atom wants to fill its electron shell. They can do this by sharing electrons.

The dot-and-cross diagram and displayed formula of H_2.

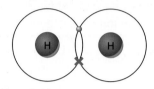

represented as

H — H

- A single covalent bond can be represented by a single line. The formula of the molecule can be written as a **displayed formula**, H–H. The hydrogen and oxygen atoms in water are also held together by single covalent bonds.

Water contains single covalent bonds.

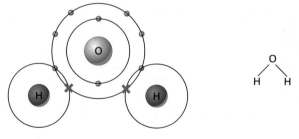

(QUESTION SPOTTER box)

QUESTION SPOTTER

- Questions on covalent bonding often ask you to draw a diagram to show how the atoms combine.
- Always draw the shared electrons in the region where the electron shells overlap.

- Some molecules contain **double covalent bonds**. In carbon dioxide, the carbon atom has an electron arrangement of 2, 4 and needs an additional four electrons to complete its outer electron shell. It needs to share its four electrons with four electrons from oxygen atoms (electron arrangement 2, 6). Two oxygen atoms are needed, each sharing two electrons with the carbon atom.

Carbon dioxide contains double bonds.

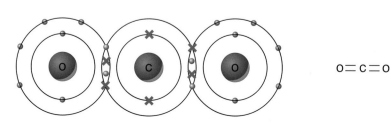

O = C = O

- Compounds containing covalent bonds have very different properties from compounds that contain ionic bonds. These differences are considered in the next section.

⌑ How many covalent bonds can an element form?

- The number of covalent bonds a non-metal atom can form is linked to its position in the periodic table. Metals (groups 1, 2, 3) do not form covalent bonds. The noble gases in group 8 are unreactive and usually don't form covalent bonds.

Group in the periodic table	1	2	3	4	5	6	7	8 (or 0)
Covalent bonds formed	X	X	X	4	3	2	1	X

A* EXTRA

▸ Non-metals can form single, double or triple covalent bonds.
▸ In a single covalent bond there are 2 shared electrons (1 pair), in a double covalent bond there are 4 shared electrons (2 pairs) and in a triple covalent bond there are 6 shared electrons (3 pairs).

❓ CHECK YOURSELF QUESTIONS

Q1 For each of the following reactions say whether the compound formed is ionic or covalent:
a hydrogen and chlorine
b carbon and hydrogen
c sodium and oxygen
d chlorine and oxygen
e calcium and bromine.

Q2 Write down the ions formed by the following elements:
a potassium
b aluminium
c sulphur
d fluorine.

Q3 Draw dot-and-cross diagrams to show the bonding in the following compounds:
a methane, CH_4
b oxygen, O_2
c nitrogen, N_2
d potassium sulphide
e lithium oxide.

Answers are on page 156.

States of matter

What are the states of matter?

- All matter is made of atoms and they are arranged differently in the three states of matter – **solids, liquids** and **gases**. The way the atoms (or particles) are arranged explains the **properties** of the three states.

- In **solids**, the particles are held tightly together in a **fixed position**, so solids have a **definite shape**. However, the particles are **vibrating** about their fixed positions because they have energy.

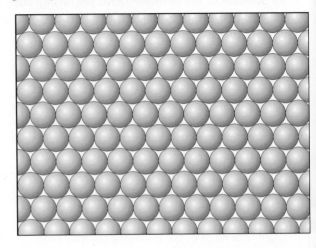

Particles in a solid.

- In **liquids**, the particles are held tightly together and have enough energy to **move around**. Liquids have **no definite shape** and will take on the shape of the container they are in.

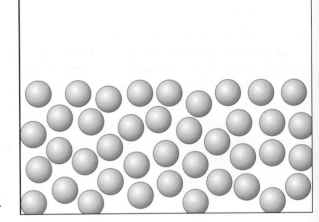

Particles in a liquid.

- In **gases**, the particles are further apart and have enough energy to **move apart** from each other. Gases can **expand** to fill the container they are in.

Particles in a gas

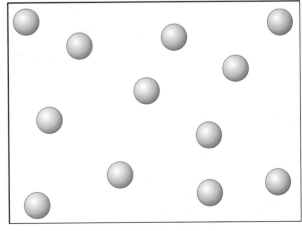

- Gases can be **compressed** to form liquids by using high pressure and cooling.

How do substances change from one state to another?

- To change solids → liquids → gases, **heat** must be put in. The heat provides the particles with enough energy to overcome the forces holding them together. The particles move **further apart** as they change from one state to another.

- These are **endothermic** processes, meaning that energy is absorbed.

- To change gases → liquids → solids involves **cooling**, so removing energy. This makes the particles come **closer together** as they change from one state to another.

- These are **exothermic** processes, meaning that energy is being given out.

- The **temperatures** at which one state changes to another have specific names:

Name of temperature	Change of state
melting point	solid → liquid
boiling point	liquid → gas
freezing point	liquid → solid
condensation point	gas → liquid

- The particles in a **liquid** can move around. They have different energies, so some are moving faster than others. The faster particles have enough energy to escape from the surface of the liquid and change into gas molecules – also called vapour molecules. This process is **evaporation**. The rate of evaporation increases with **temperature** since heating gives more particles the energy to be able to escape from the surface.

- The diagram summarises the changes in states of matter:

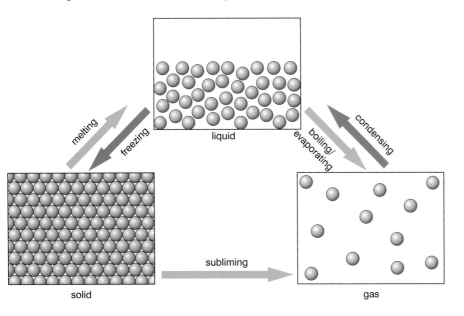

Changes of state.

■ When there is a change of state, the **temperature stays the same** as the energy is either being used to separate the particles (heating) or being released as the particles come closer together (cooling).

QUESTION SPOTTER

▸ You will be expected to use the terms for the changes of state: melting, freezing, condensing, boiling, evaporating and subliming.
▸ State symbols in equations are the usual way of showing changes, e.g. iodine subliming is: $I_2(s) \rightarrow I_2(g)$.

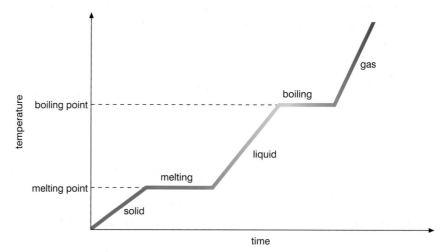

Heating curve: changes of state when heating a solid.

⚡ A* EXTRA

▸ When explaining that temperature does not change as a substance changes from one state to another, use the terms for energy changes 'exothermic' and 'endothermic'. Link this to the arrangement of particles in the substance.

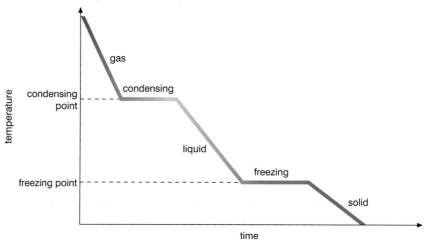

Cooling curve: changes of state when cooling a gas.

■ A substance can also change state directly from solid to gas. This change is called **sublimation**.

? CHECK YOURSELF QUESTIONS

Q1 In which state of matter do particles have the most energy? Explain your answer.

Q2 Sodium (melting point 98 °C) and aluminium (melting point 660 °C) are both metals and are solids at room temperature. From their different melting points, what can you deduce about the forces in the metals?

Q3 Steam at 100 °C causes worse burns than water at 100 °C. What is the reason for this?

Q4 Why does ice that is melting remain at 0 °C until it has all changed to water?

Q5 What change of state is taking place according to the following equation?
$Hg(g) \rightarrow Hg(l)$

Answers are on page 157.

Structures and properties

What structures do ionic compounds form?

■ Ionic compounds form **giant lattice structures**. For example, when sodium chloride is formed by ionic bonding, the ions do not pair up. Each sodium ion is surrounded by six chloride ions, and each chloride ion is surrounded by six sodium ions.

■ The electrostatic attractions between the ions are very strong. The properties of sodium chloride can be explained using this model of its structure.

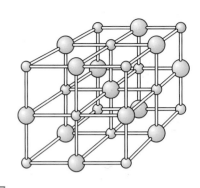

○ chloride ion   ○ sodium ion

In solid sodium chloride, the ions are held firmly in place – they are not free to move. Ionic compounds have giant ionic lattice structures like this.

Properties of sodium chloride	Explanation in terms of structure
Hard crystals	Strong forces between the ions
High melting point (801°C)	Strong forces between the ions
Dissolves in water	The water is also able to form strong electrostatic attractions with the ions – the ions are 'plucked' off the lattice structure
Does not conduct electricity when solid	Strong forces between the ions prevent them from moving
Does conduct electricity when molten or dissolved in water	The strong forces between the ions have been broken down and so the ions are able to move

Covalent compounds

■ Covalent bonds are also strong bonds. They are **intramolecular** bonds – formed *within* each molecule. There are also **intermolecular** bonds – much weaker forces *between* the individual molecules.

■ The properties of covalent compounds can be explained using a simple model involving these two types of bond or forces.

⚡ A* EXTRA

▶ Ionic compounds are electrolytes. They conduct electricity when molten or when dissolved in water (i.e. when the ions are free to move).
▶ Insoluble compounds such as calcium carbonate will only conduct electricity when they are molten.

Properties of hydrogen	Explanation in terms of structure	
Hydrogen is a gas with a very low melting point (−259°C)	The intermolecular forces between the molecules are weak	H—H — covalent bond
Hydrogen does not conduct electricity	There are no ions or free electrons present. The covalent bond (intramolecular bond) is a strong bond and the electrons cannot be easily removed from it	intermolecular force H—H

■ Some covalently bonded compounds do not exist as simple molecular structures in the way that hydrogen does. Diamond, for example, exists as a **giant structure** with each carbon atom covalently bonded to four others. The bonding is extremely strong – diamond has a melting point of about 3730 °C. Another form of carbon is graphite. Graphite has a different giant structure as seen in the diagram. Different forms of the same element are called **allotropes**.

(a) In diamond, each carbon atom forms four strong covalent bonds.

(b) In graphite, each carbon atom forms three strong covalent bonds and one weak intermolecular bond.

(a)

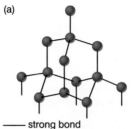

—— strong bond

(b)

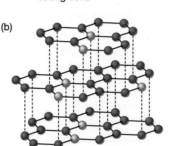

------ weak bond

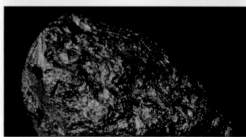

QUESTION SPOTTER

▸ A typical question will give a table of data (including melting points and boiling points) for different substances, and ask you to identify the ones that have a simple molecular structure or a giant structure.
▸ Use the melting points to decide whether they are giant structures (high melting point) or simple molecular structures (low melting point).

■ In graphite, carbon atoms form layers of hexagons in the plane of their strong covalent bonds. The weak intermolecular bonds are between the layers. Because the layers can slide over each other, graphite is flaky and can be used as a lubricant. Graphite can conduct electricity because the electrons are free to move along the layers.

■ Structures can usually be identified as being giant or molecular from their melting points.

Structure	Atom	Molecule	Ion
Giant	Diamond, graphite, metals High melting points	Sand (silicon oxide molecules) High melting point	All ionic compounds, e.g. sodium chloride High melting points
Simple molecular	Noble gases, e.g. helium Low melting points	Carbon dioxide, water Low melting points	None

Metallic bonding

■ Metals are giant structures with high melting and boiling points.

■ Metal atoms give up one or more of their electrons for form positive ions, called **cations**. The electrons they give up form a 'sea of electrons' surrounding the positive metal ions, and the negative electrons are attracted to the positive ions, holding the structure together.

- The electrons are free to move through the whole structure, which is why metals conduct electricity. The electrons are **delocalised**, meaning they are not fixed in one position.

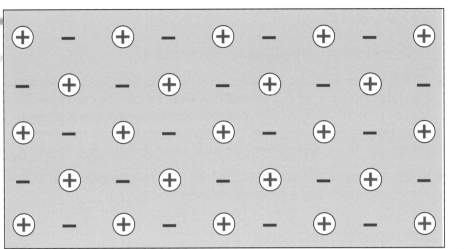

Ions and electrons in a metal.

CHECK YOURSELF QUESTIONS

Q1 Explain why an ionic substance such as potassium chloride:
   a has a high melting point
   b behaves as an electrolyte.

Q2 Use the structure of graphite to explain
   a how carbon fibres can add strength to tennis racquets
   b how graphite conducts electricity.

Q3 Explain why methane (CH_4), which has strong covalent bonds between the carbon atom and the hydrogen atoms, has a very low melting point.

Q4 Graphite can conduct electricity in only one plane but metals can conduct in all planes. Explain these facts.

Q5 Use the information in the table to answer the questions that follow.

Substance	Melting point/°C	Boiling point/°C	Electrical solid	Conducting matter
A	751	1244	poor	good
B	−50	148	poor	poor
C	630	1330	good	good
D	247	696	poor	poor

Which substance:
a is a metal
b contains ionic bonds
c has a giant covalent structure
d has a simple molecular structure?

Answers are on page 157.

UNIT 2: CHEMICAL FORMULAE AND EQUATIONS

How are chemical formulae written?

🔲 Chemical symbols and formulae

- All substances are made up from simple building blocks called **elements**. Each element has a unique **chemical symbol**, containing one or two letters. Elements discovered a long time ago often have symbols that don't seem to match their name. For example, sodium has the chemical symbol Na. This is derived from the Latin name for sodium – 'nadium'.

- When elements chemically combine they form **compounds**. A compound can be represented by a **chemical formula**.

🔲 Simple compounds

- Many compounds contain just two elements. For example, when magnesium burns in oxygen a white ash of magnesium oxide is formed. To work out the chemical formula of magnesium oxide:

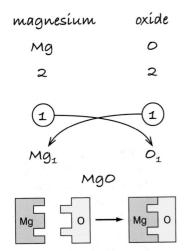

1 Write down the name of the compound.

2 Write down the chemical symbols for the elements in the compound.

3 Use the periodic table to find the 'combining power' of each element. Write the combining power of each element under its symbol.

4 If the numbers can be cancelled down, do so.

5 Swap over the combining powers. Write them after the symbol, slightly below the line (as a 'subscript').

6 If any of the numbers are 1, you do not need to write them.

Magnesium oxide has the chemical formula you would have probably guessed.

- What about calcium chloride?

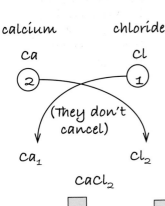

1 Write down the name of the compound.

2 Write down the chemical symbols for the elements in the compound.

3 Use the periodic table to find the 'combining power' of each element. Write the combining power of each element under its symbol.

4 If the numbers can be cancelled down, do so.

5 Swap over the combining powers. Write them after the symbol, slightly below the line (as a subscript).

6 If any of the numbers are 1, there is no need to write them.

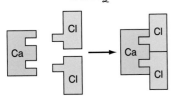

- The chemical formula of a compound is not always immediately obvious, but if you follow these rules you will have no problems.

☐ 'Combining powers' of elements

- There is a simple relationship between an element's **group number** in the periodic table and its combining power. Groups are the vertical columns in the periodic table.

Group number	I	2	3	4	5	6	7	0 (or 8)
Combining power	I	2	3	4	3	2	I	0

RULES FOR DETERMINING COMBINING POWER

- Groups 1–4: combining power = group number.

- Groups 5–8: combining power = 8 − (group number).

- If an element is not in one of the main groups, its combining power will be included in the name of the compound containing it. For example, copper is a transition metal and is in the middle block of the periodic table. In copper(II) oxide, copper has a combining power of 2.

- Sometimes an element does not have the combining power you would predict from its position in the periodic table. The combining power of these elements is also included in the name of the compound containing it. For example, phosphorus is in group 5, so you would expect it to have a combining power of 3, but in phosphorus(V) oxide its combining power is 5.

- **The only exception is hydrogen.** Hydrogen is often not included in a Group, nor is its combining power given in the name of compounds containing hydrogen. It has a combining power of 1.

- The combining power is linked to the **number of electrons** in the atom of the element.

☐ Compounds containing more than two elements

- Some elements exist bonded together in what is called a **radical**. For example, in copper(II) sulphate, the sulphate part of the compound is a radical.

- There are a number of common radicals, each having its own combining power. You cannot work out these combining powers easily from the periodic table – you have to learn them. The shaded ones in the table below are the ones you are most likely to encounter at GCSE.

QUESTION SPOTTER

▸ Questions will often expect you to write the formulae of simple compounds, usually as part of writing a fully balanced equation.
▸ To do this you will need to remember the formulae of the radicals shown in the table – they cannot easily be worked out from the periodic table.

Combining power = I		Combining power = 2		Combining power = 3	
hydroxide	OH	carbonate	CO_3	phosphate	PO_4
hydrogencarbonate HCO_3		sulphate	SO_4		
nitrate	NO_3				
ammonium	NH_4				

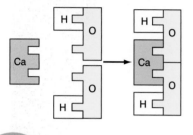

A* EXTRA

▸ In a formula containing more than one radical unit, the radical should be put in a bracket.
▸ The combining power of a radical is equal to the charge on the radical, e.g. the sulphate ion has a combining power of 2 and its formula is SO_4^{2-}.

■ The same rules apply to radicals as to elements. For example:

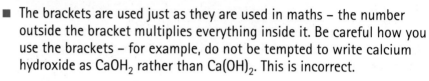

copper(II) sulphate		potassium nitrate	
Cu	SO_4	K	NO_3
2	2	I	I
$CuSO_4$		KNO_3	

■ If the formula contains **more than one radical unit**, the radical must be put in brackets. For example:

calcium hydroxide		ammonium carbonate	
Ca	OH	NH_4	CO_3
2	I	I	2
$Ca(OH)_2$		$(NH_4)_2CO_3$	

■ The brackets are used just as they are used in maths – the number outside the bracket multiplies everything inside it. Be careful how you use the brackets – for example, do not be tempted to write calcium hydroxide as $CaOH_2$ rather than $Ca(OH)_2$. This is incorrect.

$CaOH_2$ contains one Ca, one O, two H ✗

$Ca(OH)_2$ contains one Ca, two O, two H ✓

? CHECK YOURSELF QUESTIONS

Q1 Work out the chemical formulae of the following compounds:
a sodium chloride
b magnesium fluoride
c aluminium nitride
d lithium oxide
e carbon oxide (carbon dioxide).

Q2 Work out the chemical formulae of the following compounds:
a iron(III) oxide
b phosphorus(V) chloride
c chromium(III) bromide
d sulphur(VI) oxide (sulphur trioxide)
e sulphur(IV) oxide (sulphur dioxide).

Q3 Work out the chemical formulae of the following compounds:
a potassium carbonate
b ammonium chloride
c sulphuric acid
d magnesium hydroxide
e ammonium sulphate.

Answers are on page 158.

Chemical equations

⌗ Writing chemical equations

- In a **chemical equation** the starting chemicals are called the **reactants** and the finishing chemicals are called the **products**.

- Follow these simple rules to write a chemical equation.

  1 Write down the **word equation**.

  2 Write down the **symbols** (for elements) and **formulae** (for compounds).

  3 **Balance the equation**, to make sure there are the same number of each type of atom on each side of the equation.

- Many elements are **diatomic**. They exist as molecules containing two atoms.

Element	Form in which it exists
hydrogen	H_2
oxygen	O_2
nitrogen	N_2
chlorine	Cl_2
bromine	Br_2
iodine	I_2

The reaction between hydrogen and oxygen produces a lot of energy as well as water – enough to launch a rocket.

WORKED EXAMPLES

1 When a lighted splint is put into a test tube of hydrogen the hydrogen burns with a 'pop'. In fact the hydrogen reacts with oxygen in the air (the reactants) to form water (the product). Write the chemical equation for this reaction.

Word equation:	hydrogen + oxygen → water
Symbols and formulae:	$H_2 + O_2 \rightarrow H_2O$
Balance the equation:	$2H_2 + O_2 \rightarrow 2H_2O$

For every two molecules of hydrogen that react, one molecule of oxygen is needed and two molecules of water are formed.

$2H_2$	+	O_2	→	$2H_2O$
two molecules		one molecule		two molecules

2 What is the equation when natural gas (methane) burns in air to form carbon dioxide and water?

Word equation:	methane + oxygen → carbon dioxide + water
Symbols and formulae:	$CH_4 + O_2 \rightarrow CO_2 + H_2O$
Balance the equation:	$CH_4 + 2O_2 \rightarrow CO_2 + 2H_2O$

Methane is burning in the oxygen in the air to form carbon dioxide and water.

⌷ Balancing equations

■ Balancing equations can be quite tricky. Basically it is done by trial and error. However, the golden rule is that **balancing numbers can only be put in front of the formulae**.

■ For example, to balance the equation for the reaction between methane and oxygen:

	Reactants	Products
Start with the unbalanced equation.	$CH_4 + O_2$	$CO_2 + H_2O$
Count the number of atoms on each side of the equation.	1C ✓, 4H, 2O	1C ✓, 2H, 3O
There is a need to increase the number of H atoms on the products side of the equation. Put a '2' in front of the H_2O.	$CH_4 + O_2$	$CO_2 + 2H_2O$
Count the number of atoms on each side of the equation again.	1C ✓, 4H ✓, 2O	1C ✓, 4H ✓, 4O
There is a need to increase the number of O atoms on the reactant side of the equation. Put a '2' in front of the O_2.	$CH_4 + 2O_2$	$CO_2 + 2H_2O$
Count the atoms on each side of the equation again.	1C ✓, 4H ✓, 4O ✓	1C ✓, 4H ✓, 4O ✓

No atoms have been created or destroyed in the reaction. The equation is balanced!

The number of each type of atom is the same on the left and right sides of the equation.

$$CH_4 \quad + \quad 2O_2 \quad \rightarrow \quad CO_2 \quad + \quad 2H_2O$$

■ In balancing equations involving **radicals** you can use the same procedure. For example, when lead(II) nitrate solution is mixed with potassium iodide solution, lead(II) iodide and potassium nitrate are produced.

1 Words:
lead(II) nitrate + potassium iodide → lead(II) iodide + potassium nitrate

2 Symbols:
$Pb(NO_3)_2$ + KI → PbI_2 + KNO_3

3 Balance the nitrates:
$Pb(NO_3)_2$ + KI → PbI_2 + $2KNO_3$

Balance the iodides:
$Pb(NO_3)_2$ + $2KI$ → PbI_2 + $2KNO_3$

This reaction occurs simply on mixing the solutions of lead(II) nitrate and potassium iodide. Lead iodide is an insoluble yellow compound.

⊡ Ionic equations

- **Ionic equations** show reactions involving **ions** (atoms or radicals that have lost or gained electrons). The size of the charge on an ion is the same as the combining power – whether it is positive or negative depends on which part of the periodic table the element is placed in. (If you are not sure about ions, you will need to review Unit 1. You will get further practice using ionic equations in Unit 7.)

- In many ionic reactions some of the ions play no part in the reaction. These ions are called **spectator ions**. A simplified ionic equation can therefore be written, using only the important, reacting ions. In these equations, **state symbols** are often used and appear in brackets.

- The equation must **balance** in terms of chemical symbols and charges.

State	State symbol
solid	s
liquid	l
gas	g
solution	aq

States and their symbols.

QUESTION SPOTTER

▸ You are most likely to be asked to write equations including the four common state symbols.
▸ Questions may ask you to explain what a particular state symbol represents.

WORKED EXAMPLES

1 In the reaction given to produce lead(II) iodide, the potassium and nitrate ions are spectators – the important ions are the lead(II) ions and the iodide ions.

The simplified ionic equation is:

$Pb^{2+}(aq) + 2I^-(aq) \rightarrow PbI_2(s)$

Balance the equation:

	Reactants	Products
	$Pb^{2+}(aq) + 2I^-(aq)$	$PbI_2(s)$
symbols	1 Pb ✓, 2 I ✓	1 Pb ✓, 2 I ✓
charges	2^+ and $2^- = 0$ ✓	0 ✓

The equation shows that any solution containing lead(II) ions will react with any solution containing iodide ions to form lead(II) iodide.

2 Any solution containing copper(II) ions and any solution containing hydroxide ions can be used to make copper(II) hydroxide, which appears as a solid:

$Cu^{2+}(aq) + 2OH^-(aq) \rightarrow Cu(OH)_2(s)$

	Reactants	Products
	$Cu^{2+}(aq) + 2OH^-(aq)$	$Cu(OH)_2(s)$
symbols	1 Cu ✓, 2 O ✓, 2 H ✓	1 Cu ✓, 2 O ✓, 2 H ✓
charges	2^+ and $2^- = 0$ ✓	0 ✓

⚡ A* EXTRA

▸ An ionic equation only shows the ions that change in some way during the reaction – the spectator ions are not shown.
▸ The reaction between copper(II) sulphate solution and sodium hydroxide solution will have the same ionic equation as the reaction between copper(II) nitrate solution and potassium hydroxide solution.

Half equations

■ In electrolysis, the reactions at the electrodes can be shown as **half equations**.

■ For example, when copper is deposited at the **cathode** the half equation can be written as:

$$Cu^{2+}(aq) + 2e^- \rightarrow Cu(s)$$

The symbol e^- stands for an **electron**. At the cathode, positive ions gain electrons and become neutral. The equation must **balance** in terms of symbols and charges.

■ A typical reaction at the **anode** during electrolysis would be:

$$2Cl^-(aq) \rightarrow Cl_2(g) + 2e^-$$

In this reaction two chloride ions combine to form one molecule of chlorine, releasing two electrons.

■ Further examples of half equations are given in Unit 7.

CHECK YOURSELF QUESTIONS

Q1 Write symbol equations from the following word equations:
   a carbon + oxygen → carbon dioxide
   b iron + oxygen → iron(III) oxide
   c iron(III) oxide + carbon → iron + carbon dioxide
   d calcium carbonate + hydrochloric acid → calcium chloride + carbon dioxide + water.

Q2 Write ionic equations for the following reactions:
   a calcium ions and carbonate ions form calcium carbonate
   b iron(II) ions and hydroxide ions form iron(II) hydroxide
   c silver(I) ions and bromide ions form silver(I) bromide.

Q3 Write half equations for the following reactions:
   a the formation of aluminium atoms from aluminium ions
   b the formation of sodium ions from sodium atoms
   c the formation of oxygen from oxide ions
   d the formation of bromine from bromide ions.

Answers are on page 159.

UNIT 3: CHEMICAL CALCULATIONS

Atomic masses and the mole

⬚ Working out the mass of atoms

■ Atoms are far too light to be weighed. Instead scientists have developed a **relative atomic mass** scale. Initially the hydrogen atom, the lightest atom, was chosen as the unit that all other atoms were weighed in terms of.

■ On this scale, a carbon atom weighs the same as 12 hydrogen atoms, so carbon's relative atomic mass was given as 12.

■ Using this relative mass scale you can see, for example, that:

- 1 atom of magnesium has 24 × the mass of 1 atom of hydrogen
- 1 atom of magnesium has 2 × the mass of 1 atom of carbon
- 1 atom of copper has 2 × the mass of 1 atom of sulphur.

	Hydrogen	Carbon	Oxygen	Magnesium	Sulphur	Calcium	Copper
Symbol	H	C	O	Mg	S	Ca	Cu
Relative atomic mass	1	12	16	24	32	40	64

■ Recently, the reference point has been changed to carbon and the relative atomic mass is defined as:

the mass of an atom on a scale where the mass of a carbon atom is 12 units.

■ This change does not really affect the work that is done at GCSE. The relative atomic masses are not changed.

⬚ Moles of atoms

■ The **mole** is a very large number, approximately 6×10^{23}. That is 600 000 000 000 000 000 000 000.

■ 6×10^{23} atoms of hydrogen have a mass of 1 g.

■ 6×10^{23} atoms of carbon have a mass of 12 g.

■ 6×10^{23} atoms of magnesium have a mass of 24 g.

- So the relative atomic mass (RAM) of an element expressed in grams contains one mole of atoms. This means that the number of atoms of an element can be worked out by weighing.

These all contain 1 mole of atoms:

| 12 g | 24 g | 32 g | 56 g | 64 g |
| Carbon | Magnesium | Sulphur | Iron | Copper |

- Calculations can be done using the simple equation:

$$\text{moles of atoms} = \frac{\text{mass}}{\text{RAM}}$$

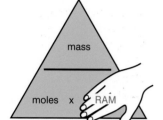

Put your finger over the quantity you are trying to work out. The triangle will then tell you whether to multiply or divide the other quantities.

WORKED EXAMPLES

1 How many moles of atoms are there in 72 g of magnesium? (RAM of magnesium = 24)

Write down the formula:	$\text{moles} = \frac{\text{mass}}{\text{RAM}}$
Rearrange if necessary:	(None needed)
Substitute the numbers:	$\text{moles} = \frac{72}{24}$
Write the answer and units:	moles = 3 moles

2 What is the mass of 0.1 moles of carbon atoms? (RAM of carbon = 12)

Write down the formula:	$\text{moles} = \frac{\text{mass}}{\text{RAM}}$
Rearrange if necessary:	$\text{mass} = \text{moles} \times \text{RAM}$
Substitute the numbers:	$\text{mass} = 0.1 \times 12$
Write the answer and units:	mass = 1.2 g

🔲 How do we work out chemical formulae?

- A chemical formula shows the number of atoms of each element that combine together. For example:

H_2O A water molecule contains 2 hydrogen atoms and 1 oxygen atom.

Alternatively:

H_2O 1 mole of water molecules is made from 2 moles of hydrogen atoms and 1 mole of oxygen atoms.

- The formula of a compound can be calculated if the number of moles of the combining elements are known.

WORKED EXAMPLES

1 What is the simplest formula of a hydrocarbon that contains 60 g of carbon combined with 20 g of hydrogen? (RAMs: H = 1, C = 12)

	C	H
Write down the mass of each element:	60	20
Work out the number of moles of each element:	$\frac{60}{12} = 5$	$\frac{20}{1} = 20$
Find the simplest ratio (divide by the smaller number):	$\frac{5}{5} = 1$	$\frac{20}{5} = 4$
Write the formula showing the ratio of atoms:		CH_4

2 What is the simplest formula of calcium carbonate if it contains 40% calcium, 12% carbon and 48% oxygen? (C = 12, O = 16, Ca = 40)

	Ca	C	O
Write down the mass of each element:	40	12	48
Work out the number of moles of each element:	$\frac{40}{40} = 1$	$\frac{12}{12} = 1$	$\frac{48}{16} = 3$
Find the simplest ratio:	(Already in the simplest ratio)		
Write the formula showing the ratio of atoms:	$CaCO_3$		

⚡ A* EXTRA

▸ When calculating moles of elements, you must be careful to make sure you know what the question is referring to. For example, you may be asked for the mass of 1 mole of nitrogen gas. N = 14, but nitrogen gas is **diatomic**, i.e. N_2, so the mass of 1 mole N_2 = 28 g. This also applies to other diatomic elements, e.g. Cl_2, Br_2, I_2, O_2 and H_2.

⬚ Moles of molecules

■ You can also refer to a mole of molecules. A mole of water molecules will be 6×10^{23} water molecules. The **relative molecular mass** of a molecule can be worked out by simply adding up the relative atomic masses of the atoms in the molecule. For example:

Water, H_2O (H = 1, O = 16)

The relative molecular mass (RMM) = 1 + 1 + 16 = 18.

Carbon dioxide, CO_2 (C = 12, O = 16)

The RMM = 12 + 16 + 16 = 44.

(Note: The '2' only applies to the oxygen atom.)

■ A similar approach can be used for any formula, including ionic formulae. As ionic compounds do not exist as molecules, the **relative formula mass** (RFM) can be worked out.

WORKED EXAMPLES

Sodium chloride, NaCl (Na = 23, Cl = 35.5)

The relative formula mass (RFM) = 23 + 35.5 = 58.5

Potassium nitrate, KNO_3 (K = 39, N = 14, O = 16)

RFM = 39 + 14 + 16 + 16 + 16 = 101

(Note: The '3' only applies to the oxygen atoms.)

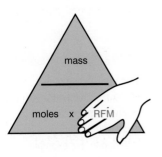

Put your finger over the quantity you are trying to work out.

Calcium hydroxide, $Ca(OH)_2$ (Ca = 40, O = 16, H = 1)

RFM = 40 + (16 + 1)2 = 40 + 34 = 74

(Note: The '2' applies to everything in the bracket.)

Magnesium nitrate, $Mg(NO_3)_2$ (Mg = 24, N = 14, O = 16)

RFM = 24 + (14 + 16 + 16 + 16)2 = 24 + (62)2 = 24 + 124 = 148

■ An equation can be written that can be used with atoms, molecules and ionic compounds.

$$\text{number of moles} = \frac{\text{mass}}{\text{RFM}}$$

CHECK YOURSELF QUESTIONS

Q1 Calculate the number of moles in the following:
  a 56 g of silicon (Si = 28)
  b 3.1 g of phosphorus (P = 31)
  c 11 g of carbon dioxide, CO_2 (C = 12, O = 16)
  d 50 g of calcium carbonate, $CaCO_3$ (Ca = 40, C = 12, O = 16)

Q2 Calculate the mass of the following:
  a 2 moles of magnesium atoms (Mg = 24)
  b 2 moles of hydrogen molecules, H_2 (H = 1)
  c 0.1 moles of sulphuric acid, H_2SO_4 (H = 1, O = 16, S = 32)

Q3 Titanium chloride contains 25% titanium and 75% chlorine by mass.
Work out the simplest formula of titanium chloride. (Ti = 48, Cl = 35.5)

Q4 Calculate the formulae of the following compounds:
  a 2.3 g of sodium reacting with 8.0 g of bromine (Na = 23, Br = 80).
  b 0.6 g of carbon reacting with oxygen to make 2.2 g of compound
  c 11.12 g of iron reacting with chlorine to make 18.22 g of compound

Answers are on page 159.

⧉ Linking reactants and products

▪ Chemical equations allow quantities of **reactants** and **products** to be linked together. They tell you how much of the products you can expect to make from a fixed amount of reactants.

▪ In a balanced equation the numbers in front of each symbol or formula indicate the number of moles represented. The number of moles can then be converted into a mass in grams.

▪ For example, when magnesium (RAM 24) reacts with oxygen (RAM 16):

Write down the balanced equation:	2Mg(s)	+ O₂(g)	→	2MgO(s)
Write down the number of moles:	2	+ 1	→	2
Convert moles to masses:	48 g	+ 32 g	→	80 g

So when 48 g of magnesium reacts with 32 g of oxygen, 80 g of magnesium oxide is produced. From this you should be able to work out the mass of magnesium oxide produced from any mass of magnesium. All you need to do is work out a **scaling factor**.

WORKED EXAMPLES

1 What mass of magnesium oxide can be made from 6 g of magnesium? (O = 16, Mg = 24.)

Equation:	2Mg(s)	+ O₂(g) →	2MgO(s)
Moles:	2	1	2
Masses:	48 g	32 g	80 g

Instead of 48 g of magnesium, the question asks about 6 g. To find the scaling factor, divide 48 by 6 = 8. So we can scale down all the quantities by dividing them by 8. Therefore $\frac{48}{8}$ g = 6 g of magnesium would make $\frac{80}{8}$ g =10 g of magnesium oxide.

Note: In this example, there was no need to work out the mass of oxygen needed. It was assumed that there would be as much as was necessary to convert all the magnesium to magnesium oxide.

2 What mass of ammonia can be made from 56 g of nitrogen? (H = 1, N = 14)

Equation:	N₂(g)	+ 3H₂(g) →	2NH₃(g)
Moles:	1	3	2
Masses:	28 g	6 g	34 g

In this case we need to multiply the mass of nitrogen by 2 to get the amount asked about in the question. Use the same scaling factor on the other quantities. So 28 g × 2 = 56 g of nitrogen makes 34 g × 2 = 68 g of ammonia.

Note: In this example there was no need to work out the mass of hydrogen required.

QUESTION SPOTTER

▸ You should be able to use equations and relative atomic masses to work out calculations like those shown here.
▸ Sometimes the question will refer to tonnes rather than grams. The method is just the same.

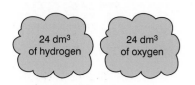

Each of these contains 1 mole (6×10^{23}) of molecules.

Moles of gases

- In reactions involving gases it is often more convenient to measure the **volume** of a gas rather than its mass.

- One mole of any gas occupies the same volume under the same conditions of temperature and pressure. The conditions chosen are usually room temperature (25 °C) and normal atmospheric pressure.

  1 mole of any gas occupies 24 000 cm³ (24 dm³) at room temperature and pressure.

- The following equation can be used to convert moles and volumes:

$$\text{moles} = \frac{\text{volume in cm}^3}{24\ 000}$$

WORKED EXAMPLE

What volume of hydrogen is formed at room temperature and pressure when 4 g of magnesium is added to excess dilute hydrochloric acid? (H = 1, Mg = 24)

Equation:	$Mg(s)$	+	$2HCl(aq)$	$\rightarrow$	$MgCl_2(aq)$	+	$H_2(g)$
Moles:	1		2		1		1
Masses/volumes:	24 g						24 000 cm³

Now work out the scaling factor needed, and use the same scaling factor on the other quantities. Here we divide 24 g by 6 to get 4 g of magnesium. This produces $\frac{24\ 000}{6}$ cm³ = 4000 cm³ of hydrogen gas.

Note: The hydrochloric acid is in excess. This means that there is enough to react with all the magnesium.

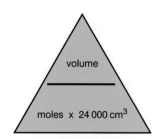

The triangle can be used as before to work out whether to multiply or divide the quantities.

Moles of solutions

- A solution is made when a **solute** dissolves in a **solvent**. The concentration of a solution depends on how much solute is dissolved in how much solvent. The concentrations of a solution is defined in terms of moles per litre (1000 cm³), or mol dm⁻³, and is referred to as the **molarity** of the solution.

  1 mole of solute dissolved to make 1000 cm³ of solution produces a 1 molar (1 M) solution

  2 moles dissolved to make a 1000 cm³ solution produces a 2 M solution

  0.5 moles dissolved to make a 1000 cm³ solution produces a 0.5 M solution

  1 mole dissolved to make a 500 cm³ solution produces a 2 M solution

  1 mole dissolved to make a 250 cm³ solution produces a 4 M solution.

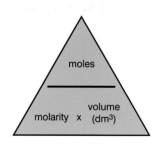

This triangle will help you to calculate concentrations of solutions.

- If the same amount of solute is dissolved to make a smaller volume of solution, the solution will be more concentrated.

WORKED EXAMPLE

How much sodium chloride can be made from reacting 100 cm³ of 1 M hydrochloric acid with excess sodium hydroxide solution? (Na = 23, Cl = 35.5)

Equation: $HCl(aq) + NaOH(aq) \rightarrow NaCl(aq) + H_2O(l)$

Moles:	1	1	1	1
Masses/volumes:	(1000 cm³ 1 M)		58.5 g	

Now work out the scaling factor and use the same scaling factor on the other quantities. In this case we divide by 10 to get 100 cm³ of reactant, which means we get $\frac{58.5}{10}$ g = 5.85 g of product.

Note: 100 cm³ of 1 M solution is equal to 0.1 mole.

CHECK YOURSELF QUESTIONS

Q1 What mass of sodium hydroxide can be made by reacting 2.3 g of sodium with water? (H = 1, O = 16, Na = 23)

$$2Na(s) + 2H_2O(l) \rightarrow 2NaOH(aq) + H_2(g)$$

Q2 Iron(III) oxide is reduced to iron by carbon monoxide. (C = 12, O = 16, Fe = 56)

$$Fe_2O_3(s) + 3CO(g) \rightarrow 2Fe(s) + 3CO_2(g)$$

  a Calculate the mass of iron that could be obtained by the reduction of 800 tonnes of iron(III) oxide.

  b What volume of carbon dioxide would be obtained by the reduction of 320 g of iron(III) oxide?

Q3 What mass of barium sulphate can be produced from 50 cm³ of 0.2 M barium chloride solution and excess sodium sulphate solution? (O = 16, S = 32, Ba = 137)

$$BaCl_2(aq) + Na_2SO_4(aq) \rightarrow$$
$$BaSO_4(s) + 2NaCl(aq)$$

Answers are on page 160.

UNIT 4: THE PERIODIC TABLE AND ITS DEVELOPMENT

Organising the elements

The story of the periodic table

- In the nineteenth century, new elements were being discovered, and chemists were trying to organise the known elements into patterns that related to similarities in their properties. **John Dalton** first suggested arranging the elements according to their **atomic masses**, from the lightest to the heaviest.

- Starting in 1817, the German chemist **Johann Dobereiner** first made the link between atomic masses and properties. He grouped elements in sets of three - **triads** - for example, chlorine, bromine and iodine. Other chemists did not accept his theory because only a few elements were known, and not all fitted into triads.

- In 1864, the British chemist **John Newlands** proposed the **law of octaves** – an idea from music – where every element had similar properties to the element eight places before or after it.

- Newlands' arrangement of some of the elements is shown below.

1	2	3	4	5	6	7
H	Li	Be	B	C	N	O
F	Na	Mg	Al	Si	P	S
Cl	K	Ca	Cr	Ti	Mn	Fe

- Newlands' table was not accepted because not all elements fitted the pattern of octaves and the link to music was ridiculed.

- In 1869, the Russian scientist **Dimitri Mendeleev** solved the problem. Like others, he grouped elements based on similar chemical properties but, importantly, his table left **gaps for elements still to be discovered**. His work is the basis for the modern periodic table.

- Because Mendeleev was using atomic masses, there were still discrepancies in the table. For example, he placed the unreactive gas argon (A_r 39.9) after potassium (A_r 39.1) and in with the reactive metals sodium and lithium.

- When the structure of the atom was better known, the elements were arranged in order of **increasing atomic number**, and then the patterns worked. (Atomic number is the number of protons in the atom.) Mendeleev had been very close with his original table.

⚡ A* EXTRA

- Questions on the development of the periodic table from Dalton to Mendeleev, and then to the modern periodic table based on atomic number, are usually set as 'extended writing', not for short (one-line) answers.
- You will be expected to write in 'good English', using correct terminology and with a logical sequence of ideas. This is a skill that needs developing, and practising on this topic will help you gain all the marks available.

✩ IDEAS AND EVIDENCE

- The development of the modern periodic table of elements is one of the most important areas of chemistry.
- For each of the major scientists involved you need to be able to quote the idea he proposed, the evidence he used for his idea and why the idea was not accepted at the time.

How are elements classified in the modern periodic table?

- Elements are the building blocks from which all materials are made. Over 100 elements have now been identified, and each element has its own properties and reactions. In the **periodic table**, elements with similar properties and reactions are put close together.

- The periodic table arranges the elements in order of increasing atomic number. As atoms are neutral, the atomic number gives the number of electrons. The elements are then arranged in **periods** and **groups**.

groups	1	2											3	4	5	6	7	0(8)
periods																		
1						H hydrogen 1												He helium 2
2	Li lithium 3	Be beryllium 4											B boron 5	C carbon 6	N nitrogen 7	O oxygen 8	F fluorine 9	Ne neon 10
3	Na sodium 11	Mg magnesium 12			transition metals								Al aluminium 13	Si silicon 14	P phosphorus 15	S sulphur 16	Cl chlorine 17	Ar argon 18
4	K potassium 19	Ca calcium 20	Sc scandium 21	Ti titanium 22	V vanadium 23	Cr chromium 24	Mn manganese 25	Fe iron 26	Co cobalt 27	Ni nickel 28	Cu copper 29	Zn zinc 30	Ga gallium 31	Ge germanium 32	As arsenic 33	Se selenium 34	Br bromine 35	Kr krypton 36
5	Rb rubidium 37	Sr strontium 38	Y yttrium 39	Zr zirconium 40	Nb niobium 41	Mo molybdenum 42	Tc technetium 43	Ru ruthenium 44	Rh rhodium 45	Pd palladium 46	Ag silver 47	Cd cadmium 48	In indium 49	Sn tin 50	Sb antimony 51	Te tellurium 52	I iodine 53	Xe xenon 54
6	Cs caesium 55	Ba barium 56	La lanthanum 57	Hf hafnium 72	Ta tantalum 73	W tungsten 74	Re rhenium 75	Os osmium 76	Ir iridium 77	Pt platinum 78	Au gold 79	Hg mercury 80	Tl thallium 81	Pb lead 82	Bi bismuth 83	Po polonium 84	At astatine 85	Rn radon 86

metal	non metal	transition metal	metalloid

Part of the modern periodic table showing periods and groups.

Periods

- Rows of elements are arranged in increasing atomic number from left to right. Rows correspond to periods which are numbered from 1 to 7.

- The first period contains only two elements, hydrogen and helium.

- The elements in the middle block of the periodic table in periods 4, 5 and 6 are called the **transition metals**.

Groups

- Columns contain elements with the atomic number increasing down the column. They are numbered from 1 to 7 and 0 (group 0 is often referred to as group 8).

- Elements in a group have similar properties – they are a 'chemical family'.

- Some groups have family names – the **alkali metals** (group 1), the **halogens** (group 7) and the **noble gases** (group 0/8).

QUESTION SPOTTER

Questions commonly ask you to label the parts of the periodic table where the metals/non-metals/transition metals are found.

- We can explain why elements in the same group have similar reactions in terms of the electron structures of their atoms (see Unit 1). Elements with the same number of electrons in their outer shells have similar chemical properties. The relationship between the group number and the number of electrons in the outer electron shell of the atom is shown in the table.

Group number	1	2	3	4	5	6	7	0 (8)
Electrons in the outer electron shell	1	2	3	4	5	6	7	2 or 8 (full)

⌂ Metals and non-metals

- Most elements can be classified as either **metals** or **non-metals**. In the periodic table, the metals are arranged on the left and in the middle, and the non-metals are on the right.

- **Metalloid** elements are between metals and non-metals. They have some properties of metals and some of non-metals. Examples of metalloids are silicon and germanium.

- Metals and non-metals have quite different physical and chemical properties.

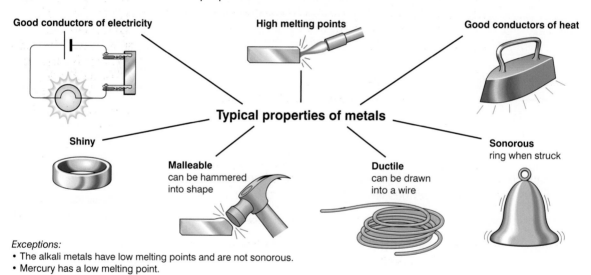

Good conductors of electricity

High melting points

Good conductors of heat

Shiny

Typical properties of metals

Sonorous
ring when struck

Malleable
can be hammered
into shape

Ductile
can be drawn
into a wire

Exceptions:
- The alkali metals have low melting points and are not sonorous.
- Mercury has a low melting point.

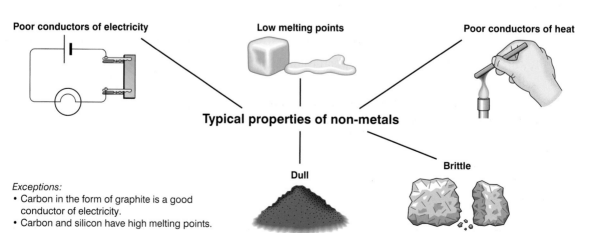

Poor conductors of electricity

Low melting points

Poor conductors of heat

Typical properties of non-metals

Brittle

Dull

Exceptions:
- Carbon in the form of graphite is a good conductor of electricity.
- Carbon and silicon have high melting points.

- The **oxides** of elements can often be made by heating the element in air or oxygen. For example, the metal magnesium burns in oxygen to form magnesium oxide:

magnesium	+	oxygen	→	magnesium oxide
$2Mg(s)$	+	$O_2(g)$	→	$2MgO(s)$

- Magnesium oxide forms as a white ash. When distilled water is added to the ash and the mixture is tested with universal indicator, the pH is greater than 7 – the oxide has formed an **alkaline** solution.

- When sulphur is burnt in oxygen, sulphur dioxide gas is formed:

sulphur	+	oxygen	→	sulphur dioxide
$S(s)$	+	$O_2(g)$	→	$SO_2(g)$

- When this is dissolved in water and then tested with universal indicator solution, the pH is less than 7 – the oxide has formed an **acidic** solution.

- The oxides of most elements can be classified as **basic oxides** or **acidic oxides**. Some elements form **neutral oxides**. For example, water is a neutral oxide. Basic oxides that dissolve in water are called **alkalis**.

- Bases and alkalis react with acids to form salts in reactions known as **neutralisation** reactions. A typical neutralisation reaction occurs when sodium hydroxide (an alkali) reacts with hydrochloric acid. The salt formed is sodium chloride, common salt:

alkali	+	acid	→	salt	+	water
sodium hydroxide	+	hydrochloric acid	→	sodium chloride	+	water
$NaOH(aq)$	+	$HCl(aq)$	→	$NaCl(aq)$	+	$H_2O(l)$

Oxide	Type of oxide	pH of solution	Other reactions of the oxide
Metal oxide	basic	more than 7 (alkaline)	reacts with an acid to form a salt + water
Non-metal oxide	acidic	less than 7 (acidic)	reacts with a base to form a salt + water

CHECK YOURSELF QUESTIONS

Q1 Explain how each of the following scientists contributed to the development of the modern periodic table.

   a John Dalton
   b Johann Dobereiner
   c John Newlands
   d Dimitri Mendeleev

Q2 What is the main difference between the way that Mendeleev arranged elements in his table, and the way atoms are arranged in the modern periodic table?

	a																
														b			
				c													d
e															f		

Q3 Look at the diagram representing the periodic table. The letters stand for elements.

   a Which element is in group 4?
   b Which element is in the second period?
   c Which element is a noble gas?
   d Which element is a transition metal?
   e Which element is a metalloid?
   f Which elements are non-metals?
   g Which element is most likely to be a gas?

Q4 Why do elements in the same group react in similar ways?

Q5 Look at the table of experimental results at the end of the question.
   a Which of the oxides is/are acidic? Explain how you decided.
   b Which of the oxides is/are basic? Explain how you decided.
   c Copper(II) oxide reacts with sulphuric acid (H_2SO_4).
      i What is the name given to this type of reaction?
      ii Write a word equation for the reaction.
      iii Write a symbol equation for the reaction.
      iv Which oxide A to D is most likely to be copper(II) oxide?

Oxide of element	pH of solution	Does it react with an acid?	Does it react with an alkali?
A	7	✓	✗
B	3	✗	✓
C	7	✗	✗
D	10	✓	✗

Answers are on page 160.

REVISION SESSION 2 ■ The metals ■

Most elements are metals. Some metals are highly reactive whilst others are almost completely unreactive. The two types of metals are found in different parts of the periodic table.

⬚ Group 1 – the alkali metals

■ These very reactive metals all have only **one electron** in their outer electron shell. This electron is readily given away when the metal reacts with non-metals. The more electrons a metal atom has to lose in a reaction, the more energy is needed to start the reaction. This is why the group 2 elements are less reactive – they have to lose two electrons when they react (see Unit 1, Revision Session 3).

■ **Reactivity increases down the group** because, as the atom gets bigger, the outer electron is further away from the nucleus and so can be removed more easily, as the atoms react and form **cations**.

⬚ Properties of group 1 metals

■ **Soft to cut**.

■ **Shiny when cut**, but quickly tarnish in the air.

■ **Very low melting points** compared with most metals.

■ **Very low densities** compared with most metals (lithium, sodium and potassium will float on water).

■ **React very easily** with air, water and elements such as chlorine. The alkali metals are so reactive that they are stored in oil to prevent reaction with air and water.

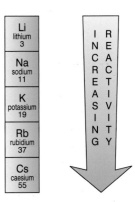

Group 1 elements become more reactive as you go further down the group.

QUESTION SPOTTER

▸ A typical question will ask you to describe what you would observe when an alkali metal is added to water.

▸ You could also be asked to write the equation for the reaction.

Reaction	Observations	Equations
Air or oxygen 	The metals burn easily with coloured flames: • lithium – red • sodium – orange • potassium – lilac A white solid oxide is formed.	lithium + oxygen → lithium oxide $4Li(s) + O_2(g) \rightarrow 2Li_2O(s)$ sodium + oxygen → sodium oxide $4Na(s) + O_2(g) \rightarrow 2Na_2O(s)$ potassium + oxygen → potassium oxide $4K(s) + O_2(g) \rightarrow 2K_2O(s)$

Reaction	Observations	Equations
Water 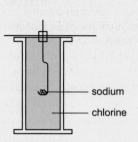	The metals react vigorously. They float on the surface, moving around rapidly. The heat of the reaction melts the metal so it forms a sphere. Bubbles of gas are given off, and the metal 'disappears'. With the more reactive metals (e.g. potassium) the hydrogen gas produced burns. The resulting solution is alkaline.	lithium + water → lithium hydroxide + hydrogen $2Li(s) + 2H_2O(l) \rightarrow 2LiOH(aq) + H_2(g)$ sodium + water → sodium hydroxide + hydrogen $2Na(s) + 2H_2O(l) \rightarrow 2NaOH(aq) + H_2(g)$ potassium + water → potassium hydroxide + hydrogen $2K(s) + 2H_2O(l) \rightarrow 2KOH(aq) + H_2(g)$
Chlorine sodium chlorine	The metals react easily, burning in the chlorine to form a white solid.	lithium + chlorine → lithium chloride $2Li(s) + Cl_2(g) \rightarrow 2LiCl(s)$ sodium + chlorine → sodium chloride $2Na(s) + Cl_2(g) \rightarrow 2NaCl(s)$ potassium + chlorine → potassium chloride $2K(s) + Cl_2(g) \rightarrow 2KCl(s)$

Uses for group 1 metals

■ The compounds of the alkali metals are widely used:

- lithium carbonate – in light sensitive lenses for glasses
- lithium hydroxide – removes carbon dioxide in air-conditioning systems
- sodium chloride – table salt
- sodium carbonate – a water softener
- sodium hydroxide – used in paper manufacture
- monosodium glutamate – a flavour enhancer
- sodium sulphite – a preservative
- potassium nitrate – a fertiliser; also used in explosives.

The transition metals

■ The transition metals are listed in the centre of the periodic table.

■ All the transition metals have **more than one electron in their outer electron shell**, which is why they are much less reactive than the alkali metals and so are more 'everyday' metals. They have much higher melting points and densities. They react much more slowly with water and with oxygen. Some, like iron, will react with dilute acids – others, like copper, show no reaction. Iron, cobalt and nickel are the only magnetic elements.

■ They are widely used as construction metals (particularly iron), and they are frequently used as **catalysts** in the chemical industry.

Property	Group I metal	Transition metal
Melting point	low	high
Density	low	high
Colours of compounds	white	coloured
Reactions with water/air	vigorous	slow or no reaction
Reactions with acid	violent (dangerous)	slow or no reaction

■ The **compounds** of the transition metals are usually **coloured**. Copper compounds are usually blue or green; iron compounds tend to be either green or brown. When sodium hydroxide solution is added to the solution of a transition metal compound, a precipitate of the metal hydroxide is formed. The colour of the precipitate will help to identify the metal. For example:

copper sulphate	+	sodium hydroxide	$\rightarrow$	copper(II) hydroxide	+	sodium sulphate
$CuSO_4(aq)$	+	$2NaOH(aq)$	$\rightarrow$	$Cu(OH)_2(s)$	+	$Na_2SO_4(aq)$

■ This can be written as an ionic equation (see page 21):

$$Cu^{2+}(aq) + 2OH^-(aq) \rightarrow Cu(OH)_2(s)$$

⚡ A* EXTRA

In this equation the sulphate ions and sodium ions are spectator ions – they play no part in the reaction. This ionic equation applies to any soluble compound containing Cu^{2+} ions.

Colour of metal hydroxide	Likely metal present
blue	copper
green	nickel
green turning to brown	iron
greenish-blue	chromium

■ Transition metal compounds and other metal compounds produce characteristic colours in **flame tests**.

Metal ion	Flame colour
lithium	red
sodium	orange/yellow
potassium	lilac
copper	turquoise
calcium	brick red
strontium	crimson
barium	green

The colour of the flame can be used to identify the metal ions present.

CHECK YOURSELF QUESTIONS

Q1 This question is about the group 1 elements.

   a Which is the most reactive of the elements?

   b Why are the elements stored in oil?

   c Which element is the easiest to cut?

   d Why do the elements tarnish quickly when they are cut?

   e Why is the group known as the alkali metals?

   f Why does sodium float when added to water?

   g Write word equations and symbol equations for the following reactions:

      i rubidium and oxygen

      ii caesium and water

      iii potassium and chlorine.

Q2 This question is about the transition metals.

   a Give two differences in the physical properties of the transition metals compared with the alkali metals.

   b Transition metals are used as catalysts. What is a catalyst?

   c Suggest why the alkali metals are more reactive than the transition metals.

Q3 Look at the table of observations below.

Compound tested	Colour of compound	Colour produced in a flame test	Effect of adding sodium hydroxide solution to a solution of the compound
A	white	orange	no change
B	green	turquoise	blue precipitate formed
C	white	brick red	white precipitate formed

   a Identify the metal present in each of the three compounds.

   b Explain why C could not contain a metal from group 1 of the periodic table.

   c Write an ionic equation for the reaction of a solution of B with sodium hydroxide solution.

Answers are on page 161.

There are only about 20 non-metal elements. There is a wide range of reactivity between different groups of non-metals. The most reactive non-metals are found in group 7, the least reactive are found in the next group, group 0.

Group 7 – The halogens

- The term 'halogen' means 'salt-maker' and the halogens react with most metals to make salts.

- The halogen elements have **seven electrons in their outermost electron shell**, so they only need to gain one electron to obtain a full outer electron shell, which makes them **very reactive**. The halogens react with metals, gaining an electron and forming a singly charged negative ion (see ionic bonding in Unit 1).

- The reactivity of the elements **decreases down the group** because, as the atom gets bigger, an eighth electron will be further from the attractive force of the nucleus. This means it is harder for the atom to gain this electron.

| F fluorine 9 |
| Cl chlorine 17 |
| Br bromine 35 |
| I iodine 53 |
| At astatine 85 |

INCREASING REACTIVITY

The elements become more reactive as you go further up the group.

Differences between the group 7 elements

- **Appearance**: fluorine is a pale yellow gas; chlorine is a yellow-green gas; bromine is a brown liquid; iodine is a black solid.

Similarities between the group 7 elements

- All have **7 electrons** in their outermost electron shell.

- All exist as **diatomic** molecules (molecules containing two atoms – e.g. F_2, Cl_2, Br_2, I_2).

- All react with water and react quickly with metals to form **salts**.

- All undergo **displacement** reactions.

⚡ **A* EXTRA**

A more reactive halogen will displace a less reactive halogen from a solution of one of its salts – for example, chlorine will displace bromine from sodium bromide solution. The ionic equation is: $Cl_2(aq) + 2Br^-(aq) \rightarrow 2Cl^-(aq) + Br_2(aq)$

Reaction	Observations	Equations
Water chlorine gas → water	The halogens dissolve in water and also react with it, forming solutions that behave as bleaches. Chlorine solution is pale yellow. Bromine solution is brown. Iodine solution is brown.	chlorine + water → hydrochloric acid + chloric(I) acid $Cl_2(g) + H_2O(l) \rightarrow HCl(aq) + HClO(aq)$
Metals chlorine iron wool	The halogens will form salts with all metals. For example, gold leaf will catch fire in chlorine without heating. With a metal such as iron, brown fumes of iron(III) chloride form.	iron + chlorine → iron(III) chloride $2Fe(s) + 3Cl_2(g) \rightarrow 2FeCl_3(s)$ Fluor*ine* forms salts called fluor*ides*. Chlor*ine* forms salts called chlor*ides*. Brom*ine* forms salts called brom*ides*. Iod*ine* forms salts called iod*ides*.

Reaction	Observations	Equations
Displacement chlorine gas → — potassium iodide solution — iodine being formed	A more reactive halogen will displace a less reactive halogen from a solution of a salt. Chlorine displaces bromine from sodium bromide solution. The colourless solution (sodium bromide) will turn brown as the chlorine is added due to the formation of bromine. Chlorine displaces iodine from sodium iodide solution. The colourless solution (sodium iodide) will turn brown as the chlorine is added due to the formation of iodine.	chlorine + sodium bromide → sodium chloride + bromine $Cl_2(g) + 2NaBr(aq) \rightarrow 2NaCl(aq) + Br_2(aq)$ chlorine + sodium iodide → sodium chloride + iodine $Cl_2(g) + 2NaI(aq) \rightarrow 2NaCl(aq) + I_2(aq)$

⌂ Uses of halogens

- The halogens and their compounds have a wide range of uses:
  - fluorides – in toothpaste help to prevent tooth decay
  - fluorine compounds – make plastics like Teflon (the non-stick surface on pans)
  - chlorofluorocarbons – propellants in aerosols and refrigerants (now being phased out due to their effect on the ozone layer)
  - chlorine – a bleach
  - chlorine compounds – kill bacteria in drinking water and are used in antiseptics
  - hydrochloric acid – widely used in industry
  - bromine compounds – make pesticides
  - silver bromide – the light sensitive film coating on photographic film
  - iodine solution – an antiseptic.

⌂ Group O – The noble gases

Name	Symbol
Helium	He
Neon	Ne
Argon	Ar
Krypton	Kr
Xenon	Xe
Radon	Rn

- This is a group of **very unreactive** non-metals. They used to be called the inert gases as it was thought that they didn't react with anything! But scientists later managed to produce fluorine compounds of some of the noble gases. As far as your school laboratory work is concerned, however, they are completely unreactive.

- This can be explained in terms of their electronic structures. The atoms all have **complete outer electron shells**. They don't need to lose electrons (as metals do), or gain electrons (as most non-metals do).

⟦⟧ Similarities of the noble gases

■ Full outer electron shells.

■ Very unreactive.

■ Gases.

■ Exist as single atoms – they are **monatomic** (He, Ne, Ar, Kr, Xe, Rn).

⟦⟧ How are the noble gases used?

■ Helium – in balloons.

■ Neon – in red tube lights.

■ Argon – in light bulbs.

■ Krypton – in some lasers.

CHECK YOURSELF QUESTIONS

Q1 This question is about the group 7 elements.

   a Which is the most reactive of the elements?

   b Which of the elements exists as a liquid at room temperature and pressure?

   c Which of the elements exists as a solid at room temperature and pressure?

   d Why are halogens such reactive elements?

   e Write word and symbol equations for the following reactions:

     i sodium and chlorine

    ii magnesium and bromine

   iii hydrogen and fluorine.

Q2 The table below records the results of some reactions.

	sodium chloride	sodium bromide	sodium iodide
chlorine	✗		✓
bromine		✗	✓
iodine			✗

A ✓ indicates a reaction occurred, a ✗ indicates no reaction occurred.

   a Give the colours of the following solutions:

     i aqueous chlorine (chlorine water)

    ii aqueous bromine

   iii aqueous iodine

   iv aqueous sodium bromide

   b What would be observed in the reaction between aqueous chlorine and sodium bromide solution?

   c Complete the table of results. Use a ✓ or ✗ as appropriate.

   d Write a word equation and symbol equation for the reaction between bromine and sodium iodide.

Q3 Explain why the noble gases are so unreactive.

Answers are on page 162.

Processing crude oil

What are fossil fuels?

- Crude oil, natural gas and coal are **fossil fuels**.

- Crude oil was formed millions of years ago from the remains of animals that were pressed together under layers of rock. It is usually found deep underground, trapped between layers of rock that it can't seep through (**impermeable** rock). Natural gas is often trapped in pockets above the crude oil.

- The supply of fossil fuels is limited – they are called 'finite' or **non-renewable** fuels. They are an extremely valuable resource which must be used efficiently.

- Fossil fuels contain many useful chemicals, and we need to separate these chemicals so that they are not wasted. For example, coal is often converted into coke by removing some of the chemicals in the coal. When the coke is burnt as a fuel, these chemicals are not wasted.

Separating the fractions

- The chemicals in crude oil are separated into useful **fractions** by a process known as **fractional distillation**.

QUESTION SPOTTER

▸ You could be asked to label the part of the fractionating column where the temperature is the highest and the parts where liquids like petrol and heavy oil are formed.

The fractionating column converts the crude oil into many useful fractions.

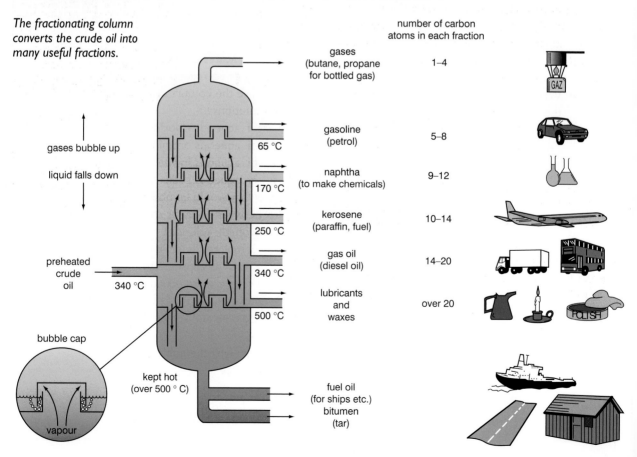

number of carbon atoms in each fraction

fraction		number of carbon atoms
gases (butane, propane for bottled gas)		1–4
gasoline (petrol)	65 °C	5–8
naphtha (to make chemicals)	170 °C	9–12
kerosene (paraffin, fuel)	250 °C	10–14
gas oil (diesel oil)	340 °C	14–20
lubricants and waxes	500 °C	over 20
fuel oil (for ships etc.) bitumen (tar)		

gases bubble up

liquid falls down

preheated crude oil   340 °C

bubble cap

kept hot (over 500 °C)

vapour

The crude oil is heated in a furnace and passed into the bottom of a
fractionating column. The vapour mixture given off rises up the column
and the different fractions condense out at different parts of the
column. The fractions that come off near the top of the column are
light-coloured runny liquids. Those removed near the bottom of the
column are dark and treacle-like. Thick liquids that are not runny,
such as these bottom-most fractions, are described as 'viscous'.

How does fractional distillation work?

The components present in crude oil separate because they have
different boiling points. A simple particle model explains why
their boiling points differ. Crude oil is a mixture of **hydrocarbon**
molecules which contain only carbon and hydrogen. The molecules
are chemically bonded in similar ways with strong covalent bonds
(see Unit 1), but contain different numbers of carbon atoms.

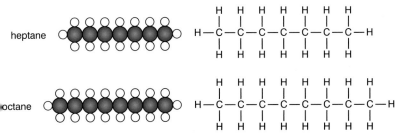

*Notice that octane has one
more carbon atom and two
more hydrogen atoms than
heptane. Their formulae differ
by CH_2.*

The weak bonds between the molecules have to be broken if the
hydrocarbon is to boil. The longer a hydrocarbon molecule is, then
the stronger the bonds are between the molecules. The stronger
these bonds, the higher the boiling point, since more energy is
needed to overcome the larger forces.

> **⚡ A* EXTRA**
>
> As a general rule, the greater
> the surface area for contact,
> the stronger the force between
> the molecules.

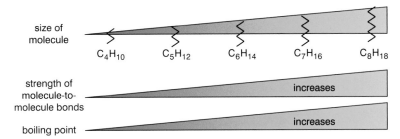

The smaller-molecule hydrocarbons more readily form a vapour – they
are more **volatile**. For example, we can smell petrol (with molecules
containing between 5 and 10 carbon atoms) much more easily than
engine oil (with molecules containing between 14 and 20 carbon atoms)
because petrol is more volatile.

■ Another difference between the fractions is how easily they burn and how smoky their flames are.

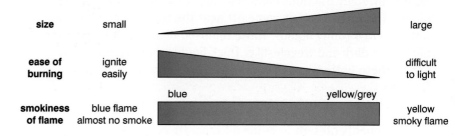

size	small	large
ease of burning	ignite easily	difficult to light
smokiness of flame	blue flame almost no smoke	yellow smoky flame

blue · · · yellow/grey

Cracking the oil fractions

■ The composition of crude oil varies in different parts of the world. The table shows the composition of a sample of crude oil from the Middle East after fractional distillation.

Fraction (in order of increasing boiling point)	Percentage produced by fractional distillation
liquefied petroleum gases (LPG)	3
petrol	13
naphtha	9
paraffin	12
diesel	14
heavy oils and bitumen	49

■ The larger molecules can be broken down into smaller ones by **cracking**. Cracking requires a **high temperature** and a **catalyst**.

The decane molecule $(C_{10}H_{22})$ is converted into the smaller molecules butane (C_4H_{10}) and propene (C_3H_6).

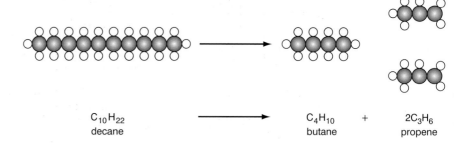

$$C_{10}H_{22} \longrightarrow C_4H_{10} + 2C_3H_6$$

decane → butane + propene

■ The butane and propene formed in this example of cracking have different types of structures. These structures will be looked at in more detail in the next session.

Reforming the molecules from cracking and oil fractions

■ **Reforming** is a process in which the **straight–chain** molecules are broken into smaller molecules which are then re-joined to form **branched–chain** molecules.

C₈H₁₈
octane

reforming

CH₃CH(CH₃)CH(CH₃)CH(CH₃)CH₃
2,3,4-trimethylpentane

The straight-chain octane molecule is reformed into a branched-chain molecule, 2,3,4-trimethylpentane.

■ The purpose of doing this is to make **high grade petrol**. The petrol fraction is a mixture of branched-chain and straight-chain molecules. Straight-chain molecules catch fire more easily than branched-chain molecules. For petrol to work efficiently, it needs to burn in the combustion chamber with oxygen at the correct temperature. This is why high-grade petrol is made of branched-chain molecules with only a few straight-chain molecules.

CHECK YOURSELF QUESTIONS

Q1 **a** How was crude oil formed?
  b Why is crude oil a non-renewable fuel?

Q2 The diagram shows a column used to separate the components present in crude oil.

a Name the process used to separate crude oil into fractions.
b What happens to the boiling point of the mixture as it goes up the column?
c The mixture of vapours arrives at level X. What now happens to the various parts of the mixture?

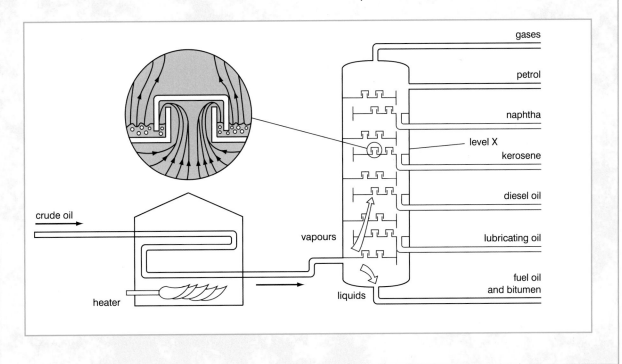

The table shows some of the properties of the crude oil components:

Component	Boiling point (°C)	How runny?	Colour	How it burns
A	up to 70	very	colourless	easily, blue flame
B	70 to 150	fairly	pale yellow	fairly easily, a smoky flame
C	150 to 230	not very	dark yellow	difficult to light, a very smoky flame

d Another component was collected between 230 °C and 300 °C.
What would it be like?

e Component A is used as a fuel in a car engine.
Suggest why component C would not be suitable as a fuel in a car engine.

Q3 The cracking of decane molecules is shown by the equation $C_{10}H_{22} \rightarrow Y + C_2H_4$
a Decane is a hydrocarbon. What is a hydrocarbon?
b What conditions are needed for cracking?
c Write down the molecular formula for hydrocarbon Y.

Q4 Reforming is an important process in refining oil.
a What happens in the reforming process?
b Give one example of when reforming is needed.

Answers are on page 163.

REVISION SESSION 2 — How are hydrocarbons used?

Combustion

■ Most of the common fuels used today are hydrocarbons – substances that contain **only** carbon and hydrogen atoms.

■ When a hydrocarbon is burnt in a plentiful supply of air it reacts with the oxygen in the air (it is **oxidised**) to form carbon dioxide and water. This reaction is an example of **combustion**.

hydrocarbon	+	oxygen	→	carbon dioxide	+	water

For example, when methane (natural gas) is burnt:

$$CH_4(g) \quad + \quad 2O_2(g) \quad \rightarrow \quad CO_2(g) \quad + \quad 2H_2O(l)$$

The complete combustion of methane in a plentiful supply of air.

■ The air contains only about 20% oxygen by volume. When a hydrocarbon fuel is burnt there is not always enough oxygen for complete combustion. Instead, some **incomplete combustion** occurs, forming **carbon** or **carbon monoxide**:

methane	+	oxygen	→	carbon monoxide	+	water
$2CH_4(g)$	+	$3O_2(g)$	→	$2CO(g)$	+	$4H_2O(l)$

methane	+	oxygen	→	carbon	+	water
$CH_4(g)$	+	$O_2(g)$	→	$C(s)$	+	$2H_2O(l)$

■ Incomplete combustion is **costly** because the full energy content of the fuel is not being released and the formation of carbon or soot reduces the efficiency of the burner being used. It can be **dangerous** as carbon monoxide is extremely poisonous. Carbon monoxide molecules attach to the haemoglobin of the blood, preventing oxygen from doing so. Brain cells deprived of their supply of oxygen will quickly die.

■ The tell-tale sign that a fuel is burning incompletely is that the flame is **yellow**. When complete combustion occurs the flame will be **blue**.

Alkanes and alkenes

■ There are two common families of hydrocarbons, the **alkanes** and the **alkenes**. Members of a family have similar chemical properties, and physical properties that change gradually from one member to the next.

■ Many alkanes are obtained from **crude oil** by **fractional distillation**. The first members of the family are used extensively as fuels. Apart from burning, however, they are remarkably unreactive. Alkanes are made up of atoms joined by single covalent bonds, so they are known as **saturated** hydrocarbons.

		Molecular formula	Displayed formula	Boiling point (°C)	State at room temperature and pressure
Alkanes	methane	CH_4		−162	gas
	ethane	C_2H_6		−89	gas
	propane	C_3H_8		−42	gas
	butane	C_4H_{10}		0	gas
	pentane	C_5H_{12}		36	liquid
Alkenes	ethene	C_2H_4		−104	gas
	propene	C_3H_6		−48	gas
	butene	C_4H_8		−6	gas
	pentene	C_5H_{10}		30	liquid

- The alkenes are often formed in the cracking process. They contain one or more carbon-carbon double bonds. Hydrocarbons with at least one double bond are known as **unsaturated** hydrocarbons. Alkenes burn well and are reactive in other ways also. Their reactivity is due to the carbon–carbon double bond.

- Alkenes can be distinguished from alkanes by adding **bromine water** to the hydrocarbon. Alkanes do not react with bromine water, but an alkene will decolourise it. The type of reaction is known as an **addition** reaction:

ethene	+	bromine	→	1,2-dibromoethane
(colourless gas)		(brown liquid)		(colourless liquid)

$$H_2C{=}CH_2 \quad + \quad Br{-}Br \quad \rightarrow \quad H{-}CH_2{-}CH_2{-}H \text{ (with Br, Br)}$$

⬚ Polymers

- Alkenes can be used to make **polymers** which are very large molecules made up of many identical smaller molecules called **monomers**. Alkenes are able to react with themselves. They join together into long chains like adding beads to a necklace. When the monomers add together like this the material produced is called an **addition polymer**. Poly(ethene) or polythene is made this way.

- By changing the atoms or groups of atoms attached to the carbon–carbon double bond, a whole range of different polymers can be made:

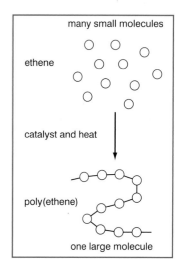

Ethene molecules link together to produce a long polymer chain of poly(ethene).

Name of monomer	Displayed formula of monomer	Name of polymer	Displayed formula of polymer	Uses of polymer
ethene	H H C=C H H	poly(ethene)	$\left(\begin{array}{cc}H & H\\ -C-C-\\ H & H\end{array}\right)_n$	buckets, bowls, plastic bags
chloroethene (vinyl chloride)	H H C=C Cl H	poly(chloroethene) (polyvinylchloride)	$\left(\begin{array}{cc}H & H\\ -C-C-\\ Cl & H\end{array}\right)_n$	plastic sheets, artificial leather
phenylethene (styrene)	H H C=C C_6H_5 H	poly(phenylethene) (polystyrene)	$\left(\begin{array}{cc}H & H\\ -C-C-\\ C_6H_5 & H\end{array}\right)_n$	yoghurt cartons, packaging
tetrafluoroethene	F F C=C F F	poly(tetrafluroethene) or PTFE	$\left(\begin{array}{cc}F & F\\ -C-C-\\ F & F\end{array}\right)_n$	non-stick coating in frying pans

QUESTION SPOTTER

▶ Questions will either give you the displayed formula of the monomer and ask you to write the displayed formula of a polymer, or will ask you to write the displayed formula of the monomer by working back from the formula of the polymer.

■ **Plastics** are very difficult to dispose of. Most of them are not **biodegradable** – they cannot be decomposed by bacteria in the soil. Currently, most waste plastic material is buried in landfill sites or is burnt, but burning plastics produces toxic fumes and landfill sites are filling up.

■ Some types of plastic can be melted down and used again. These are **thermoplastics**. Other types of plastic decompose when they are heated. These are **thermosetting** plastics. Recycling is difficult because the different types of plastic must be separated.

In thermoplastics the intermolecular bonds are weak and break on heating. The plastic can be melted and re-moulded. In thermosetting plastics the intermolecular bonds are strong interlinking covalent bonds. The whole structure breaks down when these bonds are broken by heating.

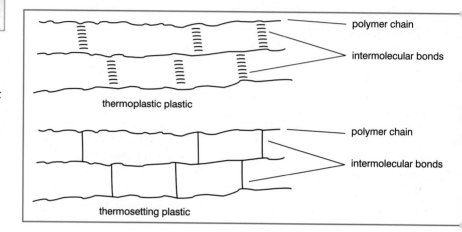

CHECK YOURSELF QUESTIONS

Q1 a Petrol is a hydrocarbon. Write a word equation for the reaction when petrol burns in a plentiful supply of air.

b When petrol is burnt in a car engine, carbon monoxide may be formed. What condition causes the formation of carbon monoxide?

c Explain what effect carbon monoxide has on the body.

Q2 a Draw displayed formulae for
  i hexane
  ii hexene.

b Describe a test that could be used to distinguish between hexane and hexene.

Q3 a Draw the displayed formula for propene.

b Write an equation using displayed formulae to show how propene can be polymerised.

c What is the name of the polymer formed in **b**?

d Explain why propane cannot form polymers as propene does.

Answers are on page 164.

UNIT 6: THE CHANGING EARTH

Geological change

⊡ Layers of the Earth

- Evidence obtained by monitoring the shock waves from earthquakes suggests that the Earth is made up of three layers: a thin rocky **crust**, the **mantle** and the **core.**

The layered structure of the Earth.

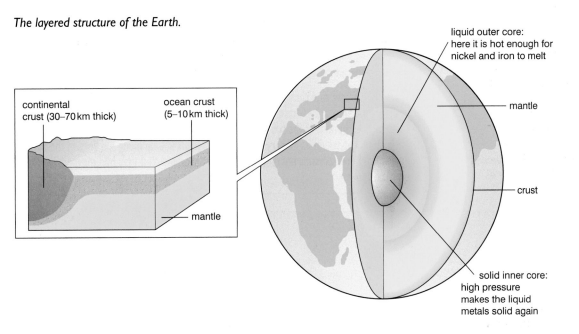

continental crust (30–70 km thick)

ocean crust (5–10 km thick)

mantle

liquid outer core: here it is hot enough for nickel and iron to melt

mantle

crust

solid inner core: high pressure makes the liquid metals solid again

- Due to large amounts of energy released by the decay of radioactive material in the core, the outer core and the mantle are in a liquid state.

- So the surface crust is really 'floating' on the liquid material of the mantle, which is called **magma**.

- Energy from the hot core is transferred out through the magma by the process of convection. This results in the formation of huge **convection currents** in the magma.

⊡ Plate tectonics

- Until the beginning of the 20th century, scientists thought that the Earth's crust had remained unchanged for millions of years. Then in 1912 the theory of **plate tectonics** was proposed.

- The crust is made up of large **tectonic plates** with boundaries between the different plates. Some plates carry continents (**continental plates**), others carry oceans (**oceanic plates**). The convection currents in the mantle cause these plates to move by a few centimetres each year. Millions of years ago, the present-day continents were joined together.

- ▸ Wegener's theory is one of the great scientific ideas of the twentieth century. Answers on this topic usually require extended writing with a mark for 'good English, sensible order and correct use of scientific terms'.
- ▸ You need to be able to present Wegener's ideas and the evidence he used for them, and compare them with the existing 'cooling' theory of the time.

Geological evidence has revealed the lines of fault where plates meet.

✦ IDEAS AND EVIDENCE

Alfred Wegener (1880–1930) proposed that 200 million years ago all the continents were joined together as one super-continent which he called Pangaea. Pangaea broke up and the continents moved apart ('continental drift').

Wegener used this evidence:
- ▸ Continental fit – the shapes of the continents seemed to match like pieces of a jigsaw.
- ▸ Fossils – the fossils of the same plants and animals are found in different continents which have different climates.
- ▸ Rocks – similar rocks were found across mountain ranges in different continents.

Wegener's ideas were not accepted at the time because the current theory was:
- ▸ the Earth was hot when it was formed so, as it cooled, the crust contracted;
- ▸ as the crust shrank it caused wrinkling, so forming mountains and other geological features;
- ▸ once hardened, the crust hardly changed;
- ▸ continents could not move through the hard and dense rock of the ocean floor.

Proof for tectonic plates and continental drift was provided in the 1960s by a drilling project into the rocks at the bottom of the oceans and seas. This is some of the evidence:
- ▸ The rocks at the bottom of the sea are younger than those of the continents.
- ▸ When molten iron solidifies and crystallises, the crystals line up along the lines of the Earth's magnetic field. Iron crystals not aligned on these lines show that they had moved from their original positions.

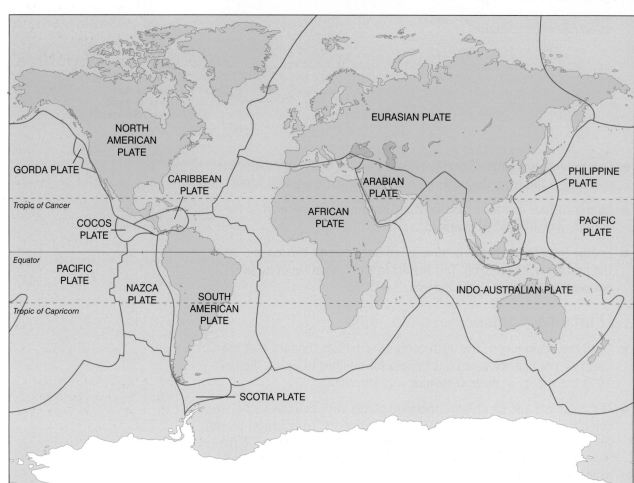

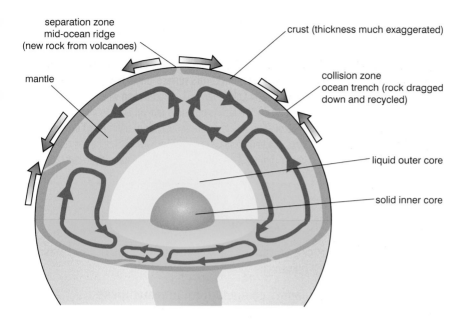

separation zone
mid-ocean ridge
(new rock from volcanoes)

crust (thickness much exaggerated)

mantle

collision zone
ocean trench (rock dragged
down and recycled)

liquid outer core

solid inner core

The huge convection currents in the mantle cause the plates to move across the surface of the Earth.

- When the tectonic plates grind together at collision zones, **earthquakes** occur. When they move apart at separation zones, a weakness or gap forms in the crust and magma forces its way up through this gap, forming a **volcano** – or, if the gap is in the ocean, a **mid-ocean ridge** is formed. If continental plates collide, **mountain ranges** can be formed – the Himalayas are thought to have been formed in this way. If the collision is between an oceanic plate and a continental plate, the denser oceanic plate is pushed down into the mantle, forming an **ocean trench**. This process is known as **subduction**.

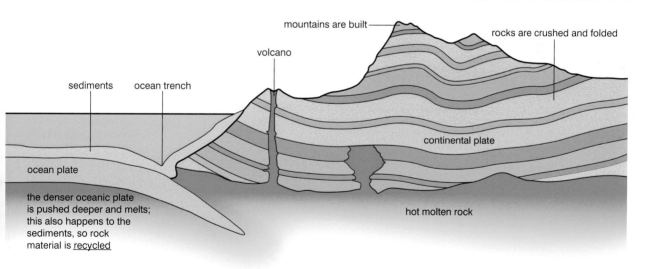

mountains are built

rocks are crushed and folded

volcano

sediments   ocean trench

continental plate

ocean plate

the denser oceanic plate is pushed deeper and melts; this also happens to the sediments, so rock material is <u>recycled</u>

hot molten rock

What happens when plates collide. This shows the process of subduction – 'drawing under'. This is happening along the west coast of North and South America.

- By locating areas of volcanic action, ocean trenches, and areas prone to earthquakes, scientists have been able to identify the separate plates and their boundaries.

QUESTION SPOTTER

▶ Questions will ask you to outline the problems of predicting where and when earthquakes and volcanoes will take place.

▶ When writing about these events you should explain the causes of earthquakes and volcanic eruptions and link these to the positions of the events, and the fact that monitoring processes cannot predict when they will occur.

IDEAS AND EVIDENCE

▶ Scientists know that earthquakes are caused when the tectonic plates rub against each other, and they occur where these fault lines cross the Earth's surface. Some lines cross populated areas such as Japan and San Francisco in California, USA, so predicting when earthquakes will happen could save lives. Unfortunately, the technology does not yet exist to do this – we don't know where earthquakes will occur (the fault lines are thousands of miles long) or when.

▶ Volcanoes are in fixed positions, so where they will erupt is known. Also, scientists constantly monitor them, so there is a better chance of knowing when they are about to erupt.

The rock cycle

■ In the **rock cycle**, rocks are constantly being broken down and new rocks are constantly forming.

■ Molten rocks in the magma cool and form **igneous rocks**.

■ **Weathering** and **erosion** produce small particles of rock, which are transported (**transportation**) by water into streams and rivers. Here they are ground into even smaller particles, which are compressed by the particles above them, eventually forming **sedimentary rock**. This process can take millions of years.

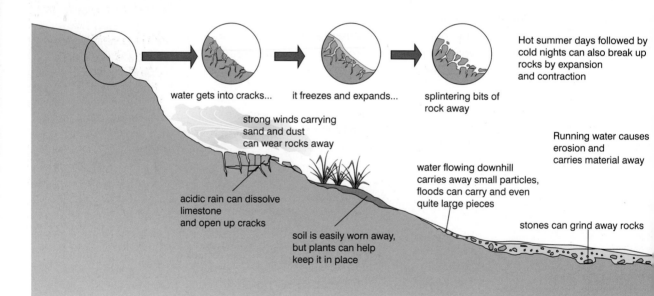

water gets into cracks...

it freezes and expands...

splintering bits of rock away

Hot summer days followed by cold nights can also break up rocks by expansion and contraction

strong winds carrying sand and dust can wear rocks away

Running water causes erosion and carries material away

acidic rain can dissolve limestone and open up cracks

water flowing downhill carries away small particles, floods can carry and even quite large pieces

stones can grind away rocks

soil is easily worn away, but plants can help keep it in place

Weathering, erosion and transportation are all important processes in the formation of sedimentary rocks.

■ When sedimentary rocks are subjected to high temperature and pressure, **metamorphic rocks** are formed. If the sedimentary or metamorphic rocks are forced close to the magma in the process of subduction, igneous rocks are formed and the rock cycle is completed.

Type of rock	Method of formation	Appearance	Examples
Igneous	Cooling of hot, liquid rock (lava from a volcano or underground magma).	Hard, containing crystals of different minerals. Crystal size depends on how quickly the molten rock crystallised. Large crystals are produced on slow cooling; small crystals are formed when the cooling is quick.	Granite, basalt.
Sedimentary	Layers of mud, sand or the shells and bones of living creatures are compressed under high pressure.	The rocks exist in layers with newer layers forming on top of older layers. Fossils are commonly found.	Limestone, sandstone.
Metamorphic	Formed from igneous and sedimentary rocks under conditions of high temperature and pressure.	Grains and crystals are often distorted and fossils are rarely present.	Marble (made from limestone), slate.

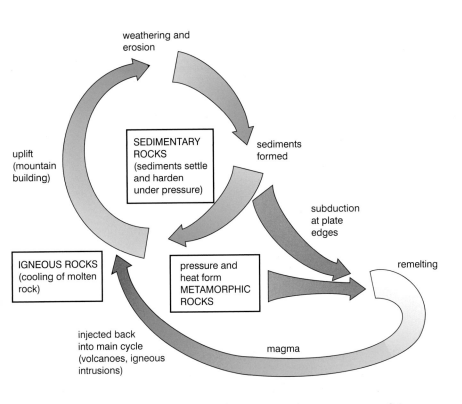

The rock cycle – the links between igneous, sedimentary and metamorphic rocks.

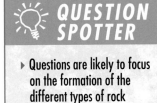

QUESTION SPOTTER

▸ Questions are likely to focus on the formation of the different types of rock and may require extended answers.
▸ When writing about the formation of sedimentary rocks you should mention the separate processes of weathering, erosion, transportation and sedimentation.

■ Evidence obtained from the structure of rocks (the **rock record**) has provided information on the age of the Earth and about the changes that have taken place over billions of years. When sedimentary rocks are formed, the lower layers are older than the upper layers. The thickness of the layers and the **fossils** they contain have provided a lot of information about the evolution of plants and animals.

CHECK YOURSELF QUESTIONS

Q1 In the diagram, A, B and C represent plates of the Earth's crust moving in the direction of the arrows.

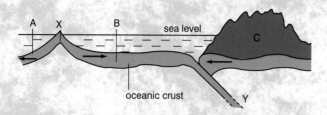

oceanic crust

a Write down one natural occurrence that could happen at the boundary between plates.

b Explain how igneous rock is formed at the plate boundary X.

c Metamorphic rock forms at Y. What two conditions are needed for the formation of metamorphic rock?

Q2 The crust of the Earth is divided into several tectonic plates.

a What causes the tectonic plates to move?

b Describe what happens to tectonic plates when they collide.

Q3 Sedimentary rock can be made from igneous rock. Three processes are involved. These are weathering, erosion and transportation. Explain how these three processes lead to the formation of sedimentary rock.

Q4 Wegener's ideas of tectonic plates and continental drift were not accepted at the time he proposed them.

a What was Wegener's theory?

b What evidence supported his theory?

c What was the current theory at the time for the geological features of the Earth?

Answers are on page 165.

☐ What is the composition of the air?

■ Air is a **mixture** of gases that has remained fairly constant for the last 200 million years. The amount of **water vapour** varies, depending where on the Earth you are. For example, a desert area has low water vapour.

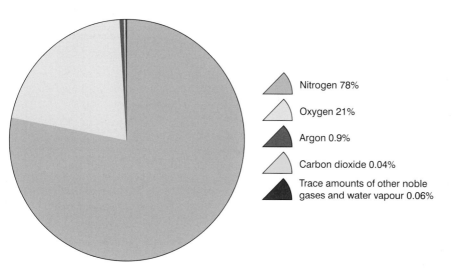

The composition of air today.

Nitrogen 78%

Oxygen 21%

Argon 0.9%

Carbon dioxide 0.04%

Trace amounts of other noble gases and water vapour 0.06%

The composition of the air is kept fairly constant by two cycles – the **nitrogen** and **carbon cycles**.

☐ The nitrogen cycle

■ Living things need nitrogen to make proteins, which are required, for example, to make new cells for growth.

■ The air is 79% nitrogen gas (N_2), but nitrogen gas is very unreactive and cannot be used by plants or animals. Instead, plants use nitrogen in the form of **nitrates** (NO_3^- ions).

■ The process of getting nitrogen into this useful form is called **nitrogen fixation**.

■ In the **nitrogen cycle** (shown on page 58):

• Nitrogen-fixing bacteria take nitrogen from the air (don't forget there is air in soil) to form nitrogen-containing compounds such as nitrates. Some of these bacteria are free-living in the soil, but some live in swellings, called root nodules, on the roots of leguminous plants, e.g. beans, peas and clover.

• Nitrifying bacteria convert ammonia from the decayed remains and waste of animals and plants into nitrates.

• Denitrifying bacteria convert nitrates back into nitrogen.

• Animals gain nitrogen when they take in protein by eating meat or plant material.

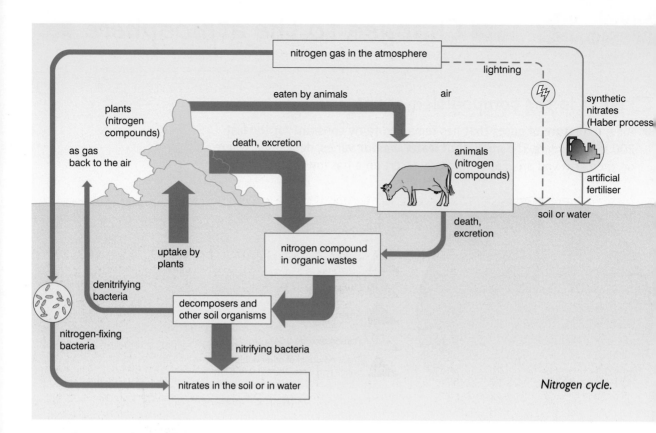

Nitrogen cycle.

▷ You may be given part of the carbon cycle or nitrogen cycle and be asked to add in the missing parts.

QUESTION SPOTTER

⟦⟧ The carbon cycle

- Plants take in carbon dioxide because they need the carbon (and oxygen) to use in **photosynthesis** to make carbohydrates and then other substances such as protein.

- When animals eat plants, they use some of the carbon-containing compounds to grow and some to release energy in respiration.

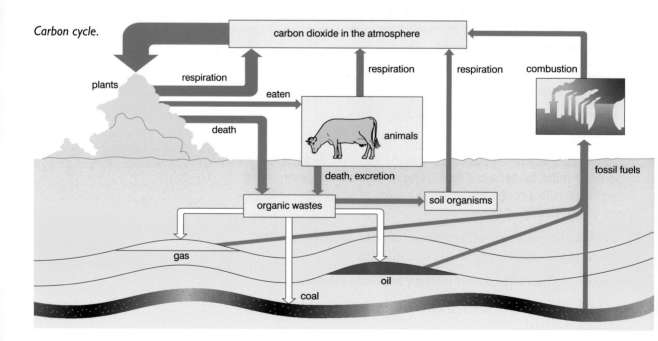

Carbon cycle.

- As a waste product of respiration, animals breathe out carbon as carbon dioxide, which is then available for plants to use. (Don't forget that plants also respire, producing carbon dioxide.)
- Carbon dioxide is also released when animal and plant remains decay (**decomposition**) and when wood, peat or fossil fuels are burnt (**combustion**).

⬚ How is the atmosphere changing, and why?

- There are two major impacts caused by the **burning of fossil fuels** – the **greenhouse effect** and **acid rain**.

⬚ The greenhouse effect

- Carbon dioxide, methane and CFCs are known as **greenhouse gases**. The levels of these gases in the atmosphere are increasing due to the burning of fossil fuels, pollution from farm animals and the use of CFCs in aerosols and refrigerators.

- Short-wave radiation from the Sun warms the ground, and the warm Earth gives off heat as long-wave radiation. Much of this radiation is stopped from escaping from the Earth by the greenhouse gases. This is known as the **greenhouse effect**.

- The greenhouse effect is responsible for keeping the Earth warmer than it would otherwise be. The greenhouse effect is normal – and important for life on Earth. However, it is thought that increasing levels of greenhouse gases are stopping even more heat escaping and that the Earth is slowly warming up. This is known as **global warming**. If global warming continues, the Earth's climate may change and sea levels rise as polar ice melts.

- The temperature of the Earth *is* gradually increasing, but we do not know for certain if the greenhouse effect is responsible. It may be that the observed rise in recent global temperatures is part of a natural cycle – there have been Ice Ages and intermediate warm periods before. Many people are concerned that it is not part of a cycle and say we should act now to reduce emissions of these greenhouse gases.

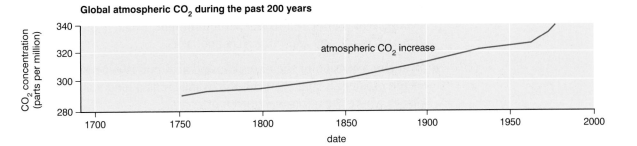

Global atmospheric CO$_2$ during the past 200 years

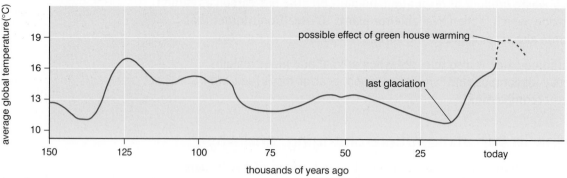

Global temperature during the past 150 000 years

possible effect of green house warming

last glaciation

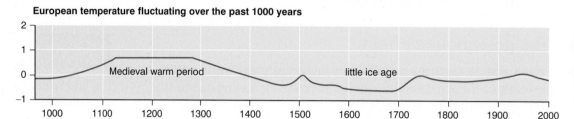

European temperature fluctuating over the past 1000 years

Medieval warm period

little ice age

⟲ Acid rain

■ Burning fossil fuels gives off many gases, including **sulphur dioxide** and various **nitrogen oxides**.

sulphur + oxygen → sulphur dioxide
$$S(s) + O_2(g) \rightarrow SO_2(g)$$

■ Sulphur dioxide combines with water to form sulphuric acid. Nitrogen oxide combines with water to form nitric acid. These substances can make the rain acidic (called **acid rain**).

sulphur dioxide + oxygen → water + sulphuric acid
$$2SO_2(g) + O_2(g) \rightarrow 2H_2O(l) + H_2SO_4(aq)$$

■ Buildings, particularly those made of limestone and marble (both are forms of calcium carbonate, $CaCO_3$), are damaged by acid rain. Metal structures are also attacked by sulphuric acid.

■ Acid rain **harms plants** that take in the acidic water and the **animals** that live in the affected rivers and lakes. Acid rain also washes ions such as calcium and magnesium out of the soil, **depleting the minerals available to plants**. It also washes **aluminium**, which is poisonous to fish, out of the soil and into rivers and lakes.

■ Reducing emission of the gases causing acid rain is expensive, and part of the problem is that the acid rain usually falls a long way from the places where the gases were given off.

■ Power stations are now being fitted with 'flue gas desulphurisation plants' (FGD), to reduce the release of sulphur dioxide into the atmosphere.

■ **Catalytic converters** fitted to vehicles reduce oxides of nitrogen to oxygen and nitrogen.

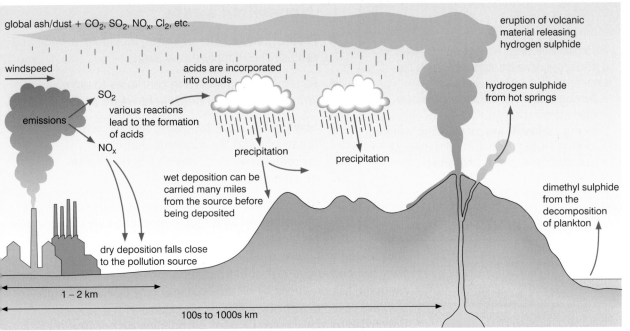

global ash/dust + CO_2, SO_2, NO_x, Cl_2, etc.

windspeed

emissions

SO_2

various reactions lead to the formation of acids

NO_x

acids are incorporated into clouds

precipitation

precipitation

wet deposition can be carried many miles from the source before being deposited

dry deposition falls close to the pollution source

eruption of volcanic material releasing hydrogen sulphide

hydrogen sulphide from hot springs

dimethyl sulphide from the decomposition of plankton

1 – 2 km

100s to 1000s km

The problem of acid rain.

⟦⟧ Depletion of the ozone layer

■ High in the atmosphere there is a layer containing a gas called **ozone**, a form of oxygen whose the molecules contain three oxygen atoms (O_3). Ozone in the atmosphere is continually being broken down and reformed:

ozone breakdown

$$O_3 \rightarrow O_2 + O$$
$$O_3 + O \rightarrow 2O_2$$

ozone formation

UV light
$$O_2 \rightarrow O + O$$
$$O_2 + O \rightarrow O_3$$

■ The ozone layer reduces the amount of **ultraviolet radiation** (UV) that reaches the Earth's surface. This is important because UV radiation can cause skin cancer.

■ Normally, the rates at which the ozone forms and breaks down are about the same. **CFCs**, which are gases used as aerosol propellants and in refrigerator cooling systems, **speed up** the rate of ozone breakdown without affecting how quickly it reforms. This means that there is **less ozone** in the atmosphere and that **more UV radiation** will be reaching the Earth's surface. This causes an increase in skin cancer in people who are exposed to a lot of sunlight.

■ We can reduce the damage to the ozone layer by finding alternatives to CFCs, but many of these seem to contribute to other problems, such as the greenhouse effect.

■ Even if all CFC emissions stopped today, it will still take around a hundred years for all the CFCs presently in the atmosphere to break down.

⚡ A* EXTRA

▸ Impurities in petrol form oxides of nitrogen when the petrol is burnt. These are sometimes referred to as NO_x, to represent compounds such as NO and NO_2. In the presence of water these can form nitric acid in the atmosphere, which contributes to acid rain.

🔆 QUESTION SPOTTER

▸ Questions on the greenhouse effect will usually require an extended written answer and may have 3 marks or more. Try to think of a separate idea for each mark – for example, what is it, what causes it, what problems does it cause?
▸ Don't confuse the greenhouse effect with the hole in the ozone layer.

IDEAS AND EVIDENCE

The impact of increasing levels of waste produced by a growing population is a major challenge to the environment. How is it to be disposed of?

▸ **Burning** it contributes to both the greenhouse effect and acid rain.

▸ Burying it in **landfill** sites just contributes to future problems, i.e. large areas of land that cannot be used again and even more land needed in the future.

▸ Replacing current non-biodegradable plastics with plastics that decay after a short time (that are **biodegradable**) will help – but is there time?

QUESTION SPOTTER

▸ Questions about environmental damage may use examples that you have not studied in detail.

▸ You will be given enough information (graphs, tables etc.), to be able to answer them.

⬚ Household waste

■ People produce a lot of waste, including sewage and rubbish they simply throw away.

■ As the Earth's population continues to increase, so will the problem of **household waste** and its **disposal**.

■ **Sewage** has to be treated to remove disease organisms and the nutrients that cause eutrophication (see page 64), before it can be discharged into the sea.

■ Some household rubbish is burnt, causing acid gas pollution and acid rain. Rubbish tips create their own problems:
  • They are ugly and can smell.
  • They can encourage rats and other pests.
  • Methane gas produced by rotting material may build up in tips that are covered with soil – this gas is explosive.
  • Covered-over tips cannot be used for building on because the ground settles.

■ We can reduce the amount of material in our dustbins by **recycling** or **reusing** materials and not buying **highly packaged** materials.

CHECK YOURSELF QUESTIONS

Q1 a In the carbon cycle, which main process removes carbon dioxide from the atmosphere?

b How is carbon dioxide put back into the atmosphere?

Q2 What is the difference between the greenhouse effect and global warming?

Q3 a Explain the cause of acid rain.
b Give two effects of acid rain.

Q4 What effect does depletion of the ozone layer have on human beings?

Answers are on page 166.

The water cycle

■ The recirculation of water that takes place all over the Earth is called the **water cycle**.

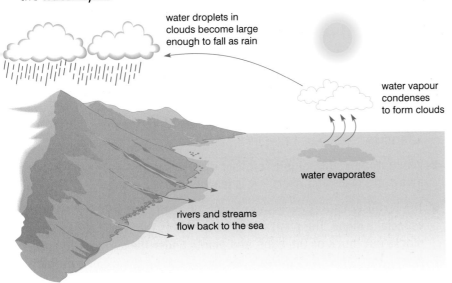

Water cycle.

water droplets in clouds become large enough to fall as rain

water vapour condenses to form clouds

water evaporates

rivers and streams flow back to the sea

■ **The rainfall pattern** over the planet determines where there will be desert regions, rainforests, and areas of land that can or cannot be used for growing plants. Ultimately, rainfall decides the **economics** of the countries of the world.

■ **Global warming** (see page 59) is thought to be responsible for **climate changes** that are affecting both where there is rainfall and how much there is of it. This could be causing both increased risks of **flooding** in some regions and **droughts** in others.

■ Water is essential for life on Earth, and the **demand for drinking water** is increasing as the world's population grows. Most **industrial processes** use water either as a raw material or for cooling processes. For example, in the United Kingdom, the amount of water used every day is 15 000 million litres, and two-thirds of this is used in the home. The rest is used by industry, for example, it takes 200 000 litres of water to make 1 tonne of steel.

■ Water stored in reservoirs needs to be purified to produce drinkable **tap water**.

QUESTION SPOTTER

▸ It is common for a question to be asked about the purification of drinking water.
▸ The use of the halogen chlorine to kill micro-organisms is specified in syllabuses. You need to remember that, for the same reason, it is also used to treat the water in swimming pools.

The treatment of water to purify it for safe drinking.

| Water from reservoirs goes to water treatment plant | ▷ | Water filtered through coarse gravel to remove larger pieces of rubbish. | ▷ | Water filtered through beds of fine gravel and sand to remove small particles. | ▷ | Chlorine passed through to kill bacteria. | ▷ | Water supply to homes and industry. |

■ In addition, tap water in certain areas of the United Kingdom is treated with sodium fluoride (NaF) to reduce tooth decay.

🔲 How is water being affected by pollution?

- **Acid rain** (see page 60) changes the pH in rivers and streams, which affects plant and animal life. It also washes aluminium ions out of the soil into the rivers and streams where it poisons fish.

- Industry uses river water in many processes, and accidental (or deliberate) leakage of chemicals into rivers and streams causes **environmental damage**.

- Farming uses increasing amounts of **fertilisers** to promote plant growth There are several reasons for this:

  - More land is under cultivation.

  - There is more demand for food as the population increases.

  - Producing larger crops in a shorter time is economically better for farmers.

- When it rains, the soluble fertiliser dissolves in the water and is carried away into lakes and rivers – it is **leached** from the soil.

- The fertiliser causes excessive growth of plants in rivers and lakes – especially **algae**. The plant overgrowth makes the water murky and blocks out much of the light, and plants under the surface die and decay. The bacteria that cause the decay use up the oxygen in the water, so fish and other water animals die.

- This whole process is called **eutrophication**.

The process of eutrophication.

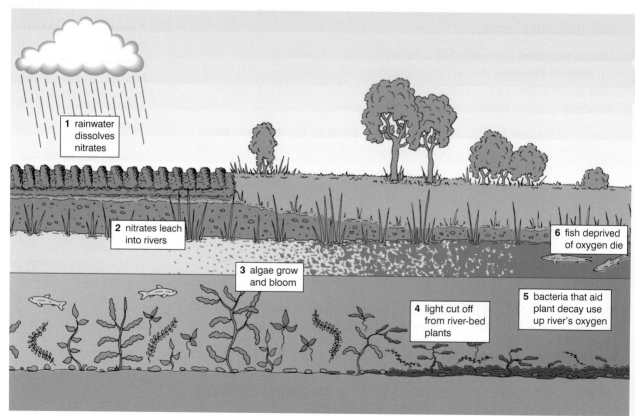

1 rainwater dissolves nitrates

2 nitrates leach into rivers

3 algae grow and bloom

4 light cut off from river-bed plants

5 bacteria that aid plant decay use up river's oxygen

6 fish deprived of oxygen die

- Eutrophication can be reduced by using **less fertiliser**. This may actually help the farmer because there is a point beyond which adding more fertiliser will not help, and may even hinder, crop growth.

IDEAS AND EVIDENCE

The increasing use of fertilisers (demand and economics) is a key issue in modern farming world-wide.
- The advantage of using more fertiliser needs to be set against the environmental damage it causes (eutrophication).
- Water contaminated with fertilisers reaches reservoirs and, without suitable treatment, tap water will contain fertilisers that can affect human health.

A* EXTRA

- Questions on this topic are usually 'extended writing' and you will gain an extra mark for 'ideas in the correct order, use of good English and the correct use of scientific terminology'. You should address the balance between the need for fertilisers and their environmental damage, as well as a clear explanation of the process of eutrophication as an environmental issue.
- In addition, you should mention that fertilisers can get into the drinking water and damage the health of those who drink it.

How is pollution affecting the seas and oceans?

- **Sea water** contains more than 'salt' (sodium chloride, NaCl). It contains a **mixture of substances** which have dissolved in water as it makes its way to the sea.

- The amount of **dissolved material** in the oceans stays approximately the same, namely about 36 g in 1 dm^3 of sea water.

- The table below shows the ions present in sea water:

- The presence of the ions in sea water enable it to keep the level of carbon dioxide at a constant level. The diagram shows the important role played by oceans absorbing carbon dioxide from the atmosphere.

Cations		Anions	
Na$^+$	85%	Cl$^-$	87%
Mg^{2+}	9%	SO$_4^{2-}$	12%
Ca^{2+}	4%	HCO$_3^-$	0.7%
K$^+$	3%	Br$^-$	0.3%

Carbon dioxide cycle.

clouds

rainwater absorbs carbon dioxide to form a weak acid – (carbonic acid)

$$H_2O + CO_2 \rightarrow H_2CO_3$$

$$H_2O_3 + Ca^{2+} + Mg^{2+}$$

Soluble hydrogencarbonates of calcium and magnesium are formed.

$$Ca(HCO_3)_2 \text{ and } Mg(HCO_3)_2$$

Insoluble carbonate of calcium is formed.

$$CaCO_3$$

– falls to the sea floor as sediment.

■ The **increase of carbon dioxide** in the atmosphere from burnt fossil fuels (that contributes to the greenhouse effect) is too rapid to be balanced by the **oceans absorbing carbon dioxide** – there is an increasing amount of carbon dioxide in the atmosphere.

■ It is still cheap to **transport** large cargoes by sea, e.g. grain and crude oil, and the number of merchant ships and tankers continues to rise. Occasionally, ships do have accidents and shed their cargoes. When a tanker carrying **crude oil** has a spill, it causes enormous environmental damage, especially if near land where it washes to shore and affects birds and other sea life.

■ After an oil spill at sea, a thin layer of oil covers a large area of the surface. If allowed to spread, it **prevents evaporation** of water and so affects the water cycle.

■ For many years around the coast of Great Britain, **raw sewage** was pumped into the sea to dispose of it. This not only damaged sea life but **polluted beaches** and affected the health of people using the sea and beaches for recreation. This practice has now virtually stopped, and an increasing number of beaches in Great Britain are gaining the European 'Blue Flag' award for being pollution-free.

? CHECK YOURSELF QUESTIONS

Q1 What are the two main physical processes that water undergoes in the water cycle?

Q2 a Give two reasons why the use of fertilisers is increasing across the world.
b Fertilisers cause eutrophication. What is eutrophication?

Q3 Explain how the seas and oceans help control the amount of carbon dioxide in the atmosphere.

Answers are on page 166.

REVISION SESSION I

What are acids, bases and alkalis?

⊡ Aqueous solutions

- When any substance dissolves in water, it forms an **aqueous solution** shown by the state symbol (aq). Aqueous solutions can be acidic, alkaline or neutral.

- **Indicators** are used to tell if a solution is acidic, alkaline or basic. Indicators can be used either as liquids or in paper form, and they become different colours with **different solutions**.

- The commonest indicator is **litmus** and its colours are shown in the table below:

Colour of litmus	Type of solution
red	acidic
purple	neutral
blue	alkaline

- **Universal Indicator** – or **UI** – can show the **strengths** of the acids and alkalis because it has more colours. Each colour is linked to a number on a scale called the **pH scale**. The range of numbers is from 1 to 14.

The pH scale.

QUESTION SPOTTER

- ▸ You are expected to know the significance of pH numbers, e.g. pH = 1 for strong acid, pH = 9 for weak alkali.
- ▸ It is particularly important for you to learn the UI colours red, green and blue/purple linked to strengths and pH numbers.

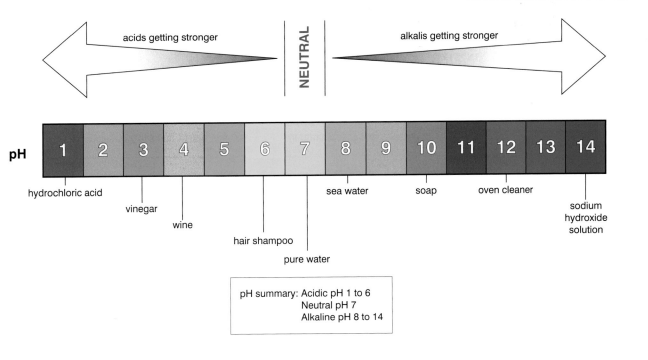

pH summary: Acidic pH 1 to 6
Neutral pH 7
Alkaline pH 8 to 14

⌨ What are acids?

- Acids are substances that contain **replaceable hydrogen atoms**. These hydrogen atoms are replaced in chemical reactions by metal atoms, and the compound formed is a **salt** (see page 71).

- Acids only show their acidic properties when **water** is present. This is because, in water, acids form hydrogen ions, H^+ (which are also **protons**) and it is these ions that are responsible for acidic properties. For example:

  $$HCl(aq) \rightarrow H^+(aq) + Cl^-(aq)$$

- **Basicity** is the term used to describe how many hydrogen ions an acid molecule can have replaced. The table shows the basicity of some common acids.

Acid	Basicity of acid
hydrochloric acid, HCl	monobasic (one H^+)
nitric acid, HNO_3	monobasic (one H^+)
sulphuric acid, H_2SO_4	dibasic (two H^+'s)
phosphoric acid, H_3PO_4	tribasic (three H^+'s)

⚡ A* EXTRA

▸ You need to be able to explain why a hydrogen ion, H^+, is also a proton. The hydrogen atom is the simplest of all the atoms — it has a nucleus of only one proton (+) with one electron (−) in the energy shell (orbit) around it. When the electron is removed, it leaves just the proton, the positive hydrogen ion, H^+.

✦ IDEAS AND EVIDENCE

▸ In 1887, the Swedish scientist Arrhenius put forward the theory that, when dissolved in water, many substances dissociated ('split up') to form ions. Other scientists did not accept his idea because they thought that water could not provide enough energy to produce the ions.

▸ However, Arrhenius still went on to propose the 'ion theory' for acids and bases. He provided definitions for them:
- An acid is a substance that, when dissolved in water, produces hydrogen ions.
- An alkali dissolves in water to produce hydroxide ions (OH^-).

▸ Two scientists called Lowry and Brønsted proposed another theory in 1923. It extended Arrhenius's ideas to situations that did not include water. These are their definitions:
- An acid is a substance that can give up a proton to a base.
- A base is any substance that can combine with a proton.

▸ This theory was more readily accepted than the original Arrhenius theory, because it explained the behaviour of substances in liquids other than water ('non-aqueous' solutions).

☐ Types of acids

- HCl, HNO_3, H_2SO_4 and H_3PO_4 are called strong acids because in water they fully dissolve (split up) into ions. They produce all the hydrogen ions available in the molecules, and this is shown by the use of the $\rightarrow$ symbol. For example:

$$HNO_3(aq) \rightarrow H^+(aq) + NO_3^-(aq)$$

$$H_2SO_4(aq) \rightarrow 2H^+(aq) + SO_4^{2-}(aq)$$

- Acids which only **partially dissociate into ions**, and so do not release all their hydrogen ions, are called **weak acids**. The molecules of these weak acids are in equilibrium with their ions, as shown by the symbol $\rightleftharpoons$ in an equation.

- Ethanoic acid, CH_3COOH, which is the acid found in vinegar, is the best-known example of a weak acid:

$$CH_3COOH(aq) \rightleftharpoons CH_3COO^-(aq) + H^+(aq)$$

☐ What are bases and alkalis?

- The oxides and hydroxides of metals are called **bases**.

- If the oxide or hydroxide of a metal dissolves in water, it is also called an **alkali**. Alkalis have pHs in the range 8–14. For example:

sodium + oxygen	$\rightarrow$	sodium oxide
$4Na(s) + O_2(g)$	$\rightarrow$	$2Na_2O(s)$

sodium oxide + water	$\rightarrow$	sodium hydroxide
$Na_2O(s) + H_2O(l)$	$\rightarrow$	$2NaOH(aq)$

- The sodium oxide above is a **base** because it is the oxide of the metal sodium. In addition, it dissolves in water to form the **alkali** sodium hydroxide.

- Arrhenius described alkalis as substances that 'dissolve in water to form hydroxide ions', OH^-. For example:

$$NaOH(aq) \rightarrow Na^+(aq) + OH^-(aq)$$

Another common alkali is potassium hydroxide, KOH.

- NaOH and KOH are **strong alkalis** because the **fully dissociate** to release all the hydroxide ions. This is shown in the equation by the use of the $\rightarrow$ symbol, in exactly the same way as for strong acids. An example is:

$$KOH(aq) \rightarrow K^+(aq) + OH^-(aq)$$

- An example of a **weak base** (weak alkali) is ammonia solution, $NH_3(aq)$, which is also called ammonium hydroxide solution, $NH_4OH(aq)$:

Either:	$NH_3(g) + H_2O(l)$	$\rightleftharpoons$	$NH_4^+(aq) + OH^-(aq)$
or:	$NH_4OH(aq)$	$\rightleftharpoons$	$NH_4^+(aq) + OH^-(aq)$

The use of the symbol $\rightleftharpoons$ shows that the reaction is in equilibrium, and so there is only **partial dissociation**.

CHECK YOURSELF QUESTIONS

Q1 **a** What is an indicator?

b What is the pH scale?

c How are Universal Indicator and the pH scale linked?

Q2 Phosphoric acid, H_3PO_4, is a strong acid.

a What is meant by a 'strong acid'?

b Write the balanced chemical equation (including state symbols) for phosphoric acid producing ions when dissolved in water.

c What would be the pH of phosphoric acid?

Q3 When lithium hydroxide, LiOH, dissolves in water, an alkaline solution is formed. Give the balanced chemical equation (including state symbols) for this reaction.

Q4 Methanoic acid, HCOOH, is a weak acid.

a What is meant by 'weak acid'?

b Write the balanced chemical equation for methanoic acid dissolving in water to produce ions.

Answers are on page 167.

REVISION SESSION 2 — Making salts

⌷ What are salts?

■ In the last session, it was explained that acids contain **replaceable hydrogen atoms**, and that when **metal atoms** take their place, a compound called a **salt** is formed. The names of salts have two parts, as shown:

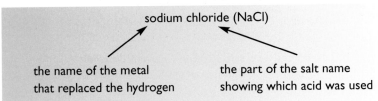

sodium chloride (NaCl)

the name of the metal that replaced the hydrogen

the part of the salt name showing which acid was used

■ The table shows the four commonest acids and their salt names.

Acid	Salt name
hydrochloric (HCl)	chloride (Cl^-)
nitric (HNO_3)	nitrate (NO_3^-)
sulphuric (H_2SO_4)	sulphate (SO_4^{2-})
phosphoric (H_3PO_4)	phosphate (PO_4^{3-})

■ Salts are **ionic compounds** where the first part of the name is of the metal ion which is a positive ion (cation), and the second part of the name is from the acid and is a negative ion (anion). For example:

copper(II) sulphate: Cu^{2+} and $SO_4^{2-} \rightarrow CuSO_4$

Sodium chloride crystals.

Copper(II) sulphate crystals.

QUESTION SPOTTER

▶ You are expected to remember the *names* of the salts formed by the four commonest acids. The formulae of the metal cations and the anions from the acids will be given to you in the examination, and you are expected then to write the chemical formula of the salt. It would be worthwhile for you to revisit Unit 2 for practice on writing formulae.

■ Salts are often found in the form of **crystals**. Salt crystals contain **water of crystallisation** which is responsible for their crystal shapes. Water of crystallisation is shown in the chemical formula of a salt. For example:

copper(II) sulphate crystals $CuSO_4.5H_2O$
iron(II) sulphate crystals $FeSO_4.7H_2O$

⬡ Methods for making salts

- There are five methods for making salts: four make **soluble salts** and one makes **insoluble salts**.

A. MAKING SOLUBLE SALTS

> 1. Acid + alkali → a salt + water
>   e.g. $HCl(aq) + NaOH(aq) \rightarrow NaCl(aq) + H_2O(l)$
>
> 2. Acid + base → a salt + water
>   e.g. $H_2SO_4(aq) + CuO(s) \rightarrow CuSO_4(aq) + H_2O(l)$
>
> 3. Acid + carbonate → a salt + water + carbon dioxide
>   e.g. $2HNO_3(aq) + K_2CO_3(s) \rightarrow 2KNO_3(aq) + H_2O(l) + CO_2(g)$
>
> 4. Acid + metal → a salt + hydrogen
>   e.g. $2HCl(aq) + Mg(s) \rightarrow MgCl_2(aq) + H_2(g)$

- The four general equations above are best remembered by the initials of the reactants:

> A (acid) + A (alkali)
> A (acid) + B (base)
> A (acid) + C (carbonate)
> A (acid) + M (metal)

- The symbol '(aq)' after the formula of the salt shows that it is a **soluble salt**.

- **Neutralisation** is the specific term used for the reactions of **acids** with **alkalis** and **bases**. When acids react with alkalis, the reaction is between H^+ ions and OH^- ions to make water, as:

> $H^+(aq) + OH^-(aq) \rightarrow H_2O(l)$

- Reactions of acids with alkalis are used in the experimental procedure of **titration**, in which solutions react together to give the end-point shown by an indicator. Calculations are then performed to find the concentration of the acid or the alkali (see Unit 3, Chemical calculations).

Apparatus for a titration.

3. MAKING INSOLUBLE SALTS

■ If two solutions of **soluble salts** are mixed together forming two new salts and one of the products is **insoluble**, the **insoluble salt** forms a **precipitate** – a 'solid made in solution'; see an example on page 20. The general equation is:

$$\text{soluble} + \text{soluble} \rightarrow \text{insoluble} + \text{soluble}$$
$$\text{salt} \qquad \text{salt} \qquad \text{salt} \qquad \text{salt}$$
$$\text{(precipitate)}$$

For example:

$$Na_2CO_3(aq) + CuSO_4(aq) \rightarrow CuCO_3(s) + Na_2SO_4(aq)$$

■ The **state symbols** show the salts in solution as (aq) and the precipitate – the insoluble salt – as (s).

⌂ Making salts in the laboratory

A. SOLUBLE SALTS

■ Of the *four* methods for making soluble salts, symbol (aq), only *one* uses solution A(aq) + solution B(aq).

Method 1 (neutralisation):

$$\text{acid(aq)} + \text{alkali(aq)} \rightarrow \text{a salt(aq)} + \text{water(l)}$$

■ The other three methods involve adding a solution(aq) to a solid(s).

Method 2:

$$\text{acid(aq)} + \text{base(s)} \rightarrow \text{a salt(aq)} + \text{water(l)}$$

Method 3:

$$\text{acid(aq)} + \text{carbonate(s)} \rightarrow \text{a salt(aq)} + \text{water(l)} + \text{carbon dioxide(g)}$$

Method 4:

$$\text{acid(aq)} + \text{metal(s)} \rightarrow \text{a salt(aq)} + \text{hydrogen(g)}$$

■ The flow diagram shows how to make soluble salts from solids, namely in Methods 2, 3 and 4.

Making soluble salts.

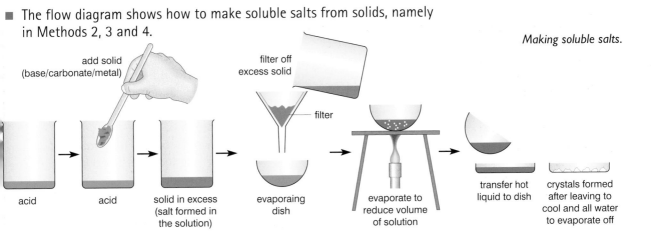

add solid (base/carbonate/metal)

filter off excess solid

filter

acid | acid | solid in excess (salt formed in the solution) | evaporaing dish | evaporate to reduce volume of solution | transfer hot liquid to dish | crystals formed after leaving to cool and all water to evaporate off

B. INSOLUBLE SALTS

■ Method 5 involves making a precipitate of an insoluble salt by mixing solutions of two soluble salts:

> soluble + soluble → insoluble + soluble
> salt(aq)   salt(aq)   salt(s)   salt(aq)
>   (precipitate)

■ The flow diagram shows how to make an insoluble salt.

Making insoluble salts.

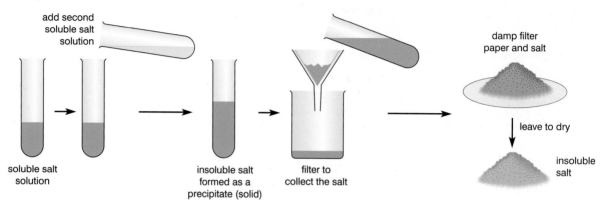

add second
soluble salt
solution

damp filter
paper and salt

leave to dry

soluble salt
solution

insoluble salt
formed as a
precipitate (solid)

filter to
collect the salt

insoluble
salt

CHECK YOURSELF QUESTIONS

Q1 Complete the following equations and include state symbols:

    a $2KOH(aq) + H_2SO_4(aq) \rightarrow$ _____ + _____

    b $2HCl(aq) + MgO(s) \rightarrow$ _____ + _____

    c $2HNO_3(aq) + BaCO_3(s) \rightarrow$ _____ + _____ + _____

    d $2HCl(aq) + Zn(s)$ _____ + _____

    e $ZnCl_2(aq) + K_2CO_3(aq) \rightarrow$ _____ + _____

Q2 Describe how you would make a sample of copper(II) sulphate crystals in the laboratory starting with copper(II) oxide powder and dilute sulphuric acid. Your answer should include any pieces of apparatus used.

Q3 Write the balanced chemical equations (including state symbols) for the preparation of the following salts:
    a zinc sulphate from solid zinc
    b potassium chloride from potassium hydroxide solution
    c copper(II) nitrate from copper(II) carbonate
    d magnesium carbonate from magnesium chloride solution and potassium carbonate solution
    e zinc chloride from solid zinc oxide

Answers are on page 167.

Sodium chloride and the chlor-alkali industry

⊡ How do we obtain sodium chloride?

- Sodium chloride, NaCl, is the best known of all the 'salt family' and is the reason it is known as **common salt**. From earliest times it has been used to preserve and flavour foodstuffs.

- The human body needs a minimum amount of salt to maintain **health**.

- Sodium chloride is found in the **oceans** and **seas** and in **land deposits** which were once covered by the oceans.

- Solid sodium chloride is **extracted** in three main ways:

  1 In hotter climates, **sea water** is poured into large flat open tanks and the heat from the sun **evaporates** off the water.

  Land deposits are underground and the salt is obtained in the following ways.

  2 The solid salt is **mined** and dug out, then purified by dissolving it in water to produce sodium chloride solution, called **brine**.

  3 It is obtained by **solution mining** if the deposits are deep under the ground.

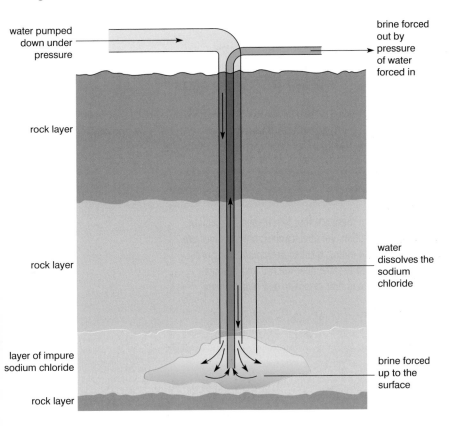

water pumped down under pressure

brine forced out by pressure of water forced in

Solution mining.

rock layer

rock layer

water dissolves the sodium chloride

layer of impure sodium chloride

brine forced up to the surface

rock layer

⬚ What happens when sodium chloride solution (brine) is electrolysed?

■ When sodium chloride dissolves in water, its **ions** separate:

$$NaCl(aq) \rightarrow Na^+(aq) + Cl^-(aq)$$

There are also some ions from the water:

$$H_2O(l) \rightleftharpoons H^+(aq) + OH^-(aq)$$

■ In the process of **electrolysis**, ions are converted to atoms. In the case of brine:

Na$^+$ and H$^+$ are attracted to the cathode (−)

Cl$^-$ and OH$^-$ are attracted to the anode (+).

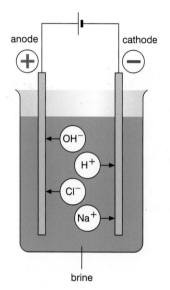

The electrolysis of sodium chloride solution (brine).

At the cathode (−)
Sodium is more reactive than hydrogen, so only the **hydrogen ions** are changed to atoms to form a molecule:

$$2H^+(aq) + 2e^- \rightarrow H_2(g)$$

At the anode (+)
Both OH$^-$ and Cl$^-$ are attracted to the anode, but only the **chloride ions** are changed to atoms to form a molecule:

$$2Cl^-(aq) \rightarrow Cl_2(g) + 2e^-$$

The remaining solution contains the ions Na$^+$ and OH$^-$, so it is sodium hydroxide solution, NaOH(aq).

Summary   At the cathode: hydrogen gas
               At the anode: chlorine gas
               The solution: sodium hydroxide

■ The electrolysis of brine is a very important industrial process and is the basis of the **chlor–alkali industry**, which is the large-scale production of chlorine, hydrogen and sodium hydroxide.

🔆 QUESTION SPOTTER

It is very common for questions on the electrolysis of brine to include the *chemical test* for three products. You need to remember these tests and their results:
▸ chlorine gas – bleaches damp blue litmus paper
▸ hydrogen gas – 'pops' with a lighted splint
▸ sodium hydroxide solution – turns Universal Indicator blue/purple.

⚡ A* EXTRA

▸ The fact that there are four ions involved in sodium chloride solution, yet in electrolysis only two ions are converted to atoms, is called *preferential discharge*.
▸ You will need to remember the two ions that are discharged and that *oxidation* and *reduction* are involved:
   $2Cl^-(aq) \rightarrow Cl_2(g) + 2e^-$ = *oxidation of* Cl$^-$
   $2H^+(aq) + 2e^- \rightarrow H_2(g)$ = *reduction of* H$^+$

⬚ The chlor-alkali industry

- The large-scale manufacture of chlorine, hydrogen and sodium hydroxide by the electrolysis of brine involves collecting the three substances and ensuring *they do not mix together* as they are produced in the electrolytic cell.

- The two main electrolytic cells used in industry are:

1 The **mercury cell**

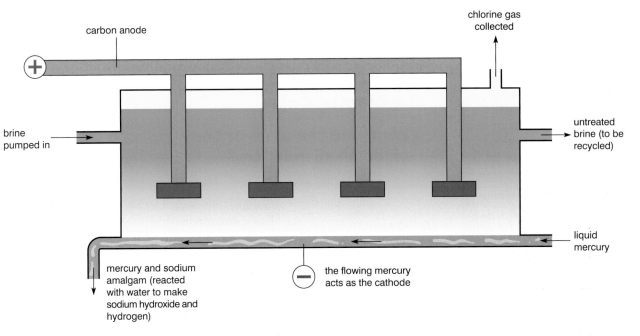

2 The **membrane cell**

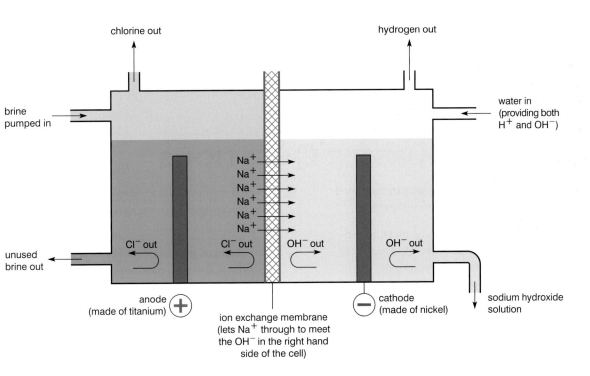

■ Both processes are very **efficient**, since there is little waste produced (the unused brine and mercury are recycled). The major **cost** is the electricity used.

■ Both the mercury cell and the membrane cell produce chlorine, hydrogen and sodium hydroxide.

■ The *major difference* between the two cells is that the membrane cell produces the three substances from the cell, while the mercury cell extracts the sodium as an amalgam. The amalgam of sodium and mercury is then reacted with water:

> sodium + water → sodium hydroxide + hydrogen gas

This means the mercury cell is a more indirect method than the membrane cell.

⌷ What are the uses of the products of the chlor-alkali industry?

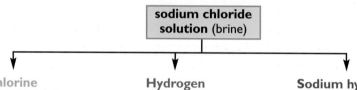

sodium chloride solution (brine)

Chlorine
• killing bacteria in water
• making – bleaches
    – paints
    – dyes
    – hydrochloric acid
    – pharmaceuticals

Hydrogen
• making – nylon
    – margarine
    – hydrogen peroxide
    – ammonia

Sodium hydroxide
• purifying natural gas
• sewage treatment
• degreasing metals
• making – paper
    – soaps and detergents
    – aluminium

? CHECK YOURSELF QUESTIONS

Q1 Explain why sodium chloride can be mined using 'solution mining', but coal cannot.

Q2 **a** Write the reactions taking place at the cathode and anode in the electrolysis of sodium chloride solution (brine).
b Explain how sodium hydroxide solution is formed during the electrolysis of brine.

Q3 Where does the term 'chlor-alkali' come from?

Q4 Why is it important to keep the products of the electrolysis of brine apart in the industrial electrolytic cells?

Q5 For each gas, give the chemical test used to identify it, *and* give one large-scale use for it:
a chlorine
b hydrogen

Answers are on page 168.

Extraction of metals

How are metals extracted?

- Metals are found in the form of **ores** containing **minerals** mixed with unwanted rock. In almost all cases, the mineral is a compound of the metal, not the pure metal. One exception is gold, which exists naturally in a pure state.

- Extracting a metal from its ore usually involves two steps:
  1 The mineral is physically separated from unwanted rock
  2 The mineral is chemically broken down to obtain the metal.

Reactivity of metals

- The chemical method chosen to break down a mineral depends on the reactivity of the metal. The **more reactive** a metal is, the **harder** it is to break down its compounds. The more reactive metals are obtained from their minerals by the process of **electrolysis**.

- The less reactive metals can be obtained by heating their oxides with carbon. This method will only work for metals below carbon in the **reactivity series**. It involves the **reduction** of a metal oxide to the metal.

> **QUESTION SPOTTER**
>
> ▸ The most frequently asked questions test understanding of the relationship between the method chosen for extracting a metal from its ore and the reactivity of that metal.

Metal	Extraction method
potassium sodium calcium magnesium aluminium	The most reactive metals are obtained using electrolysis.
(carbon)	
zinc iron tin lead copper	These metals are below carbon in the reactivity series and so can be obtained by heating their oxides with carbon.
silver gold	The least reactive metals are found as pure elements.

Using carbon to extract copper

- Copper is extracted by heating the mineral **malachite** (copper(II) carbonate) with carbon. The reaction takes place in two stages:

Stage 1 – The malachite decomposes:

copper(II) carbonate → copper(II) oxide + carbon dioxide
$$CuCO_3(s) \rightarrow CuO(s) + CO_2(g)$$

Stage 2 – The copper(II) oxide is reduced by the carbon:

copper(II) oxide + carbon → copper + carbon dioxide
$$2CuO(s) + C(s) \rightarrow 2Cu(s) + CO_2(g)$$

- The copper produced by this process is purified by electrolysis (see page 83).

⬚ The blast furnace

- Iron is produced on a very large scale by reduction using carbon. The reaction takes place in a huge furnace called a **blast furnace**.

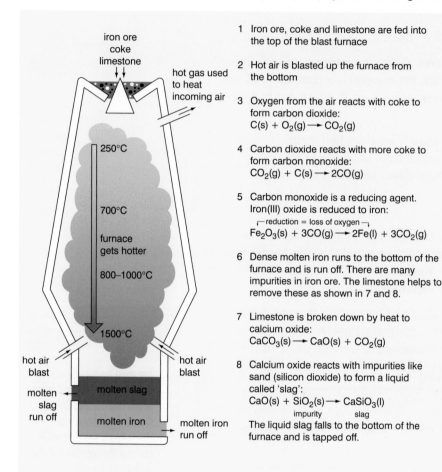

iron ore
coke
limestone

hot gas used to heat incoming air

250°C

700°C

furnace gets hotter

800–1000°C

1500°C

hot air blast

hot air blast

molten slag run off

molten slag

molten iron

molten iron run off

1. Iron ore, coke and limestone are fed into the top of the blast furnace

2. Hot air is blasted up the furnace from the bottom

3. Oxygen from the air reacts with coke to form carbon dioxide:
$$C(s) + O_2(g) \longrightarrow CO_2(g)$$

4. Carbon dioxide reacts with more coke to form carbon monoxide:
$$CO_2(g) + C(s) \longrightarrow 2CO(g)$$

5. Carbon monoxide is a reducing agent. Iron(III) oxide is reduced to iron:
reduction = loss of oxygen
$$Fe_2O_3(s) + 3CO(g) \longrightarrow 2Fe(l) + 3CO_2(g)$$

6. Dense molten iron runs to the bottom of the furnace and is run off. There are many impurities in iron ore. The limestone helps to remove these as shown in 7 and 8.

7. Limestone is broken down by heat to calcium oxide:
$$CaCO_3(s) \longrightarrow CaO(s) + CO_2(g)$$

8. Calcium oxide reacts with impurities like sand (silicon dioxide) to form a liquid called 'slag':
$$CaO(s) + SiO_2(s) \longrightarrow CaSiO_3(l)$$
impurity   slag
The liquid slag falls to the bottom of the furnace and is tapped off.

- Three important raw materials are put in the top of the furnace: **iron ore** (iron(III) oxide, the source of iron), **coke** (the source of carbon needed for the reduction) and **limestone**, needed to remove the impurities as a 'slag'.

A blast furnace is used to reduce iron(III) oxide to iron.

- The overall reaction is:

iron oxide	+	carbon	→	iron	+	carbon dioxide
$2Fe_2O_3(s)$	+	$3C$	→	$4Fe$	+	$3CO_2$

- The reduction happens in three stages.

Stage 1 – The coke (carbon) reacts with oxygen 'blasted' into the furnace:

carbon	+	oxygen	→	carbon dioxide
$C(s)$	+	$O_2(g)$	→	$CO_2(g)$

Stage 2 – The carbon dioxide is reduced by unreacted coke to form carbon monoxide:

carbon dioxide	+	carbon	→	carbon monoxide
$CO_2(g)$	+	$C(s)$	→	$2CO(g)$

Stage 3 – The iron(III) oxide is reduced by the carbon monoxide to iron:

iron(III) oxide	+	carbon monoxide	→	iron	+	carbon dioxide
$Fe_2O_3(s)$	+	$3CO(g)$	→	$2Fe(s)$	+	$3CO_2(g)$

Making steel from iron

- Iron from the blast furnace is **brittle** and **corrodes** very easily because it contains a large percentage of carbon (from the coke).

- The corrosion of iron is called **rusting** and it is a chemical reaction between iron, water and oxygen. Common ways of protecting iron from rusting are:

  - **Galvanising** – covering iron in zinc. The zinc corrodes instead of the iron if the coating is damaged. This is called **sacrificial protection**.

  - **Alloying** – mixing iron with other metals to make steel.

- In **steel making**, the molten iron (pig iron) straight from the blast furnace is heated, and oxygen is passed through it to remove some of the large percentage of carbon present after the iron is extracted:

  $$C(s) + O_2(g) \rightarrow CO_2(g)$$

- Steel is iron with 0.1–1.5% carbon content. Steel is more resistant to corrosion and is less brittle than iron. It has a wide range of uses, depending on its carbon content. For example:

  low carbon (<0.3%) – car bodies
  medium carbon (0.3 – 0.9%) – rail tracks
  high carbon (0.9 – 1.5%) – knives

- **Stainless steels** are made by adding a wide range of metals to steel such as chromium, nickel, vanadium and cobalt. Each one gives the steel particular properties for specific uses. For example, vanadium steel is used to make high precision, hard-wearing industrial tools.

Extraction of other metals

- Lead and zinc are also extracted in large quantities by heating their oxides with carbon.

- Metals that are above carbon in the reactivity series cannot be obtained by heating their oxides with carbon. They are reduced by **electrolysis**. Electrolysis is the breakdown of a chemical compound by an electric current.

Conditions for electrolysis

- The substance being electrolysed (the **electrolyte**) must contain ions and these ions must be free to move. In other words, the substance must either be molten or dissolved in water.

- A d.c. voltage must be used. The **electrode** connected to the **positive** terminal of the power supply is known as the **anode**. The electrode connected to the **negative** terminal of the power supply is known as the **cathode**. The electrical circuit can be drawn as shown on the next page.

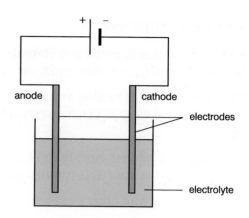

A typical electrical circuit used in electrolysis.

How does the electrolyte change?

■ The negative ions are attracted to the anode and release electrons. (Loss of electrons is oxidation.) For example:

chloride ions $\rightarrow$ chlorine molecules + electrons

$$2Cl^-(aq) \quad \rightarrow \quad Cl_2(g) \quad + \quad 2e^-$$

■ The positive ions are attracted to the cathode and gain electrons. (Gaining electrons is reduction.) For example:

copper ions + electrons $\rightarrow$ copper atoms

$$Cu^{2+}(aq) \quad + \quad 2e^- \quad \rightarrow \quad Cu(s)$$

■ The electrons move through the external circuit from the anode to the cathode.

Extracting aluminium

■ Aluminium is extracted from the ore **bauxite** (aluminium oxide) by electrolysis. The aluminium oxide is insoluble, so it is **melted** to allow the ions to move when an electric current is passed through it. The anodes are made from carbon and the cathode is the carbon-lined steel case.

The extraction of aluminium is expensive. A mineral called cryolite is added to the aluminum oxide to lower the melting point and save energy costs.

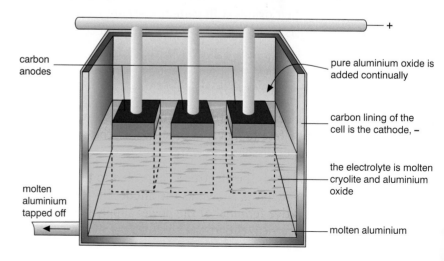

At the cathode **aluminium** is formed:

aluminium ions	+	electrons	→	aluminium
$Al^{3+}(l)$	+	$3e^-$	→	$Al(l)$

At the anode **oxygen** is formed:

oxide ions	→	oxygen molecules	+	electrons
$2O^{2-}(l)$	→	$O_2(g)$	+	$4e^-$

The oxygen reacts with the carbon anodes to form carbon dioxide. The rods constantly need to be replaced because of this.

Using electrolysis to purify copper

Copper is extracted from its ore by reduction with carbon, but the copper produced is not pure enough for some of its uses, such as making electrical wiring. It can be purified using electrolysis.

The impure copper is made the anode in a cell with copper(II) sulphate as an electrolyte. The cathode is made from a thin piece of pure copper.

At the anode the copper atoms dissolve, forming copper ions:

copper atoms	→	copper ions	+	electrons
$Cu(s)$	→	$Cu^{2+}(aq)$	+	$2e^-$

At the cathode the copper ions are deposited to form copper atoms:

copper ions	+	electrons	→	copper atoms
$Cu^{2+}(aq)$	+	$2e^-$	→	$Cu(s)$

Copper is purified by electrolysis.

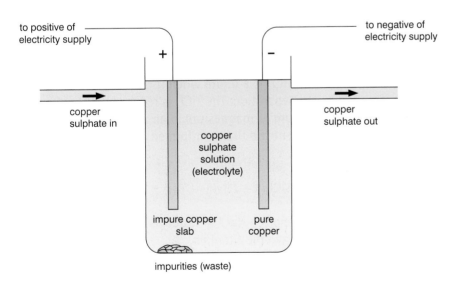

to positive of electricity supply

to negative of electricity supply

+

−

copper sulphate in

copper sulphate out

copper sulphate solution (electrolyte)

impure copper slab

pure copper

impurities (waste)

- Titanium is a transition metal which is **strong**, **light** (has a low density) and **resistant to corrosion**. These properties make it a very important metal when used either on its own or mixed with other metals to make **alloys**.

- The **properties** of titanium mean it can be used for replacement hip joints, making aircraft, lining pipes and tanks in chemical factories and sports equipment such as bicycles.

- Titanium is found as titanium oxide, TiO_2, in its **ore** which is called rutile.

- Titanium is above carbon in the reactivity series, so it cannot be extracted like iron.

- Most reactive metals – like aluminium – are produced by **electrolysis**. This method cannot be used because TiO_2 is **covalently** bonded, so cannot conduct electricity.

- The method for extracting titanium uses the fact that titanium is *below* the group 1 metals (including sodium) and the group 2 metals (including magnesium) in the reactivity series.

- These are the steps in the extraction of titanium:

  1 The crushed ore (rutile) is heated with carbon and chlorine gas is passed over the mixture at above 900 °C:

  $$TiO_2(s) + C(s) + 2Cl_2(g) \rightarrow TiCl_4(g) + CO_2(g)$$

  2 The titanium(IV) chloride, $TiCl_4$, is also a **covalent** compound. It is separated from the carbon dioxide gas by fractional distillation.

  3 The $TiCl_4$ is a **liquid** when it is condensed after the separation. The $TiCl_4$ is reduced with molten **sodium** or **magnesium** in an atmosphere of **argon** (to prevent the titanium formed oxidising back to TiO_2):

  $$TiCl_4(l) + 4Na(l) \rightarrow Ti(s) + 4NaCl(l)$$

  $$or\ TiCl_4(l) + 2Mg(l) \rightarrow Ti(s) + 2MgCl_2(l)$$

  The molten NaCl or $MgCl_2$ is run off, to leave the titanium.

CHECK YOURSELF QUESTIONS

Q1 Iron is made from iron ore (iron oxide) in a blast furnace by heating with carbon.

  a Write a word equation for the overall reaction.

  b Is the iron oxide oxidised or reduced in this reaction? Explain your answer.

  c Why is limestone also added to the blast furnace?

Q2 Explain the following terms:

  a electrolysis

  b electrolyte

  c electrode

  d anode

  e cathode.

Q3 Aluminium is extracted from aluminium oxide (Al_2O_3) by electrolysis. Aluminium oxide contains Al^{3+} and O^{2-} ions. The aluminium oxide is heated until it is in a molten state.

  a Why is the electrolysis carried out on molten rather than solid aluminium oxide?

  b Which electrode does the aluminium form at?

  c Explain how aluminium atoms are formed from aluminium ions. Write an ionic equation for this change.

  d The carbon electrodes need to be replaced regularly. Explain why.

Q4 Titanium is found in the rock rutile as titanium oxide, TiO_2.

  a Why is electrolysis not used to extract titanium from TiO_2 in the way that it is used to extract aluminium from its ore aluminium oxide, Al_2O_3?

  b Describe how titanium is extracted from rutile, and give the two relevant chemical equations.

  c Explain why the extraction of titanium from rutile can be described as a reduction process.

Answers are on page 169.

The limestone industry

The cliffs at Dover show the huge depth of chalk that built up millions of years ago.

What is limestone?

- Metals are not the only substances extracted from the Earth's rocks. A very important mineral is **limestone**. Limestone, chalk and marble are all forms of **calcium carbonate, $CaCO_3$**.

- The three forms of calcium carbonate were all formed millions of years ago in the oceans, from the remains of **sea organisms** such as coral and the shells of other sea creatures.

- As they died and fell to the sea floor, large layers of calcium carbonate built up, and were then covered by layers of other rocks. The different pressures of the overlying rock layers turned the calcium carbonate into chalk, limestone or marble.

- As the oceans retreated and the surface of the Earth changed, some of these deposits became part of land masses, sometimes many miles from the sea.

- For many centuries, limestone has been **quarried** as blocks for use in buildings and statues.

St Paul's Cathedral in London is built from marble.

QUESTION SPOTTER

▸ You should be able to describe the formation of limestone millions of years ago in the oceans.
▸ The *environmental issues* are commonly examined, and you need to explain why cathedrals, for example, are having to be restored (*pollution* effect). In addition, you should be able to discuss the environmental issue of limestone quarrying in areas of natural beauty.

- To give an idea of limestone's importance, in the UK, over 65 million tonnes of limestone are quarried every year - only a small proportion of the amount quarried all over the world. Quarrying is an **environmental issue** since it changes the landscape. The Peak District is a National Park but is also a source of limestone quarrying.

- Old buildings made of limestone are damaged by the effect of **pollution**, particularly by acid rain. Calcium carbonate reacts with acids, so the buildings are being chemically attacked and worn away.

⌑ What are the uses of limestone and its products?

- Limestone is still used for buildings in some areas, but the major uses of calcium carbonate and its products are in a wide range of **industries**.

- For centuries, limestone has been heated in lime kilns to make 'quicklime' or calcium oxide, CaO:

$$CaCO_3(s) \xrightarrow{1200\ °C} CaO(s) + CO_2(g)$$
limestone   quicklime

This is an example of **thermal decomposition**, namely the use of heat ('thermal') to break up a substance.

- A modern rotary kiln is shown below.

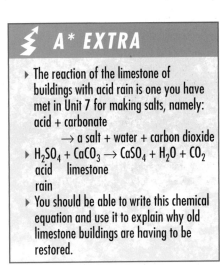

A rotary kiln for making quicklime.

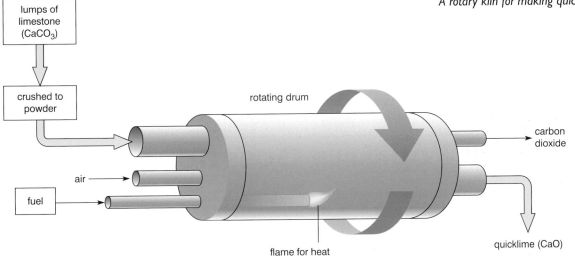

▸ The many purposes served by limestone, quicklime and slaked lime explain why vast amounts are used every year throughout the world.

▸ A question on this topic will always ask you to give one or two uses for one or more of the three compounds. You should look at the uses for each and decide which two you can most easily remember for the examination. 'Neutralise acidity' should be one, because this is the same for all three compounds.

■ When **water** is added to calcium oxide (quicklime), a vigorous **exothermic** (heat-producing) reaction takes place, and **slaked lime** – calcium hydroxide, $Ca(OH)_2$, is formed.

$$CaO(s) + H_2O(l) \rightarrow Ca(OH)_2(s)$$
quicklime   slaked lime

Slaked lime is an **alkali**, which is the basis of many of its uses.

■ The **major uses** of limestone, quicklime and slaked lime are given below

Limestone ($CaCO_3$)
* crushed and used as **aggregate** for road building
* added as a powder to lakes to **neutralise acidity**
* mixed with clay to make **cement**
* used to extract iron in the **blast furnace**
* heated with soda and sand to make **glass**
* used to **neutralise acid gases**, e.g. SO_2 produced by power stations

Quicklime (CaO)
* added to soil to **neutralise acidity**
* used in making **steel** from iron
* used as **drying agent** in industry

Slaked lime ($Ca(OH)_2$)
* added to soil to **neutralise acidity**
* used in **mortar** for building
* used to make **pottery**
* in solution, it is called **limewater**, used for tests for carbon dioxide, $CO_2(g)$

▸ You need to recognise that, in the list of uses for the three compounds, most involve chemical reactions. These need to be quoted to make a better answer about 'uses'. The following are examples.

Limestone in power stations:
$$CaCO_3 + H_2SO_4 \rightarrow CaSO_4 + H_2O + SO_2$$
$$\left(\begin{array}{l} H_2O + SO_2 \rightarrow H_2SO_3 \\ 2H_2SO_3 + O_2 \rightarrow 2H_2SO_4 \end{array}\right)$$
Quicklime as a drying agent:
$$CaO + H_2O \rightarrow Ca(OH)_2$$
Slaked lime as 'limewater' to test for carbon dioxide:
$$Ca(OH)_2 + CO_2 \rightarrow CaCO_3 + H_2O$$

▸ $CaCO_3$ is insoluble in water and is the cause of the cloudy/milky colour seen in limewater when CO_2 is present.

? CHECK YOURSELF QUESTIONS

Q1 Why are millions of tonnes of limestone quarried every year worldwide?

Q2 Write the balanced chemical equations, including state symbols, for the following:
a changing limestone into quicklime
b changing quicklime into slaked lime.

Q3 a Describe the limewater test for carbon dioxide.
b Write the word equation and the balanced chemical reaction (including state symbols) for the reaction occurring in the limewater test.

Q4 How is limestone used in power stations?

Answers are on page 170.

UNIT 9: CHEMICAL REACTIONS

— Chemical change

▢ What happens in chemical reactions?

- A chemical change, or **chemical reaction**, is quite different from the physical changes that occur, for example, when sugar dissolves in water.

FEATURES OF A CHEMICAL REACTION

- One or more **new substances** are produced.

- In many cases an **observable change** is apparent, for example the colour changes or a gas is produced.

- An **apparent change in mass** can occur. This change is often quite small and difficult to detect unless accurate balances are used. Mass is conserved in a chemical reaction – the apparent change in mass usually occurs because one of the reactants or products is a gas.

- An **energy change** is almost always involved. In most cases energy is released and the surroundings become warmer. In some cases energy is absorbed from the surroundings and so the surroundings become colder. Note: Some physical changes, such as evaporation, also produce energy changes.

▢ Collision theory

- For a chemical reaction to occur, the reacting particles (atoms, molecules or ions) must **collide**. The energy involved in the collision must be enough to break the chemical bonds in the reacting particles – or the particles will just bounce off one another.

- A collision that has enough energy to result in a chemical reaction is an **effective collision**.

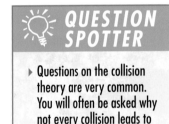

QUESTION SPOTTER

▸ Questions on the collision theory are very common. You will often be asked why not every collision leads to a reaction.

unsuccessful

successful

Particles must collide with sufficient energy to make an effective collision.

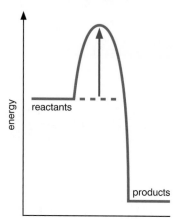

energy

reactants

products

course of reaction

If the activation energy of a reaction is low, more of the collisions will be effective and the reaction will proceed quickly. If the activation energy is high a smaller proportion of collisions will be effective and the reaction will be slow.

■ Some chemical reactions occur extremely quickly (for example, the explosive reaction between petrol and oxygen in a car engine) and some more slowly (for example, iron rusts over days or weeks). This is because they have different **activation energies**. Activation energy is the minimum amount of energy required in a collision for a reaction to occur. As a general rule, the bigger the activation energy the slower the reaction will be at a particular temperature.

Rate of a reaction

■ A quick reaction takes place in a short time. It has a high **rate of reaction**. As the time taken for a reaction to be completed increases, the rate of the reaction decreases. In other words:

$$\text{rate} \propto \frac{1}{\text{time}}$$

Speed	Rate	Time
quick or fast	high	short
slow	low	long

Monitoring the rate of a reaction

■ When marble (calcium carbonate) reacts with hydrochloric acid, the following reaction starts straight away:

calcium carbonate	+	hydrochloric acid	→	calcium chloride	+	carbon dioxide	+	water
$CaCO_3(s)$	+	$2HCl(aq)$	→	$CaCl_2(aq)$	+	$CO_2(g)$	+	$H_2O(l)$

■ The reaction can be monitored as it proceeds either by measuring the **volume of gas** being formed or by measuring the **change in mass** of the reaction flask.

The volume of gas can be measured every 10 seconds.

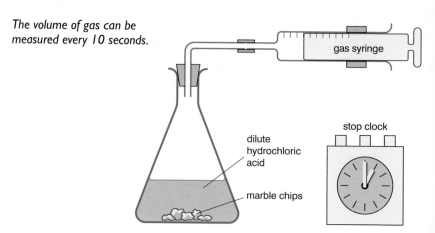

gas syringe

dilute hydrochloric acid

marble chips

stop clock

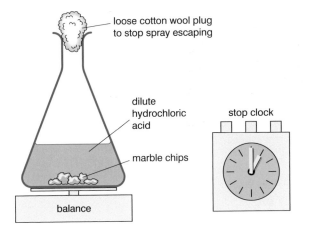

loose cotton wool plug to stop spray escaping

dilute hydrochloric acid

stop clock

marble chips

balance

The change in mass can be measured every 10 seconds. The carbon dioxide produced in the reaction escapes into the air. The cotton wool plug is there to stop acid spray from escaping.

Graphs of the results from both experiments have almost identical shapes.

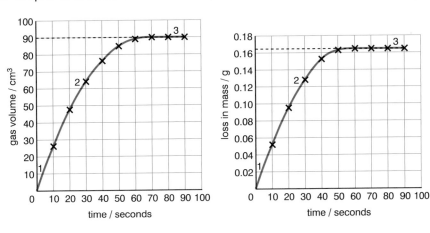

The rate of the reaction decreases as the reaction proceeds.

The **rate of the reaction** at any point can be calculated from the **gradient** of the curve. The shapes of the graphs can be divided into three regions:

1 At this point, the curve is the steepest (has the greatest gradient) and the reaction has its highest rate. The maximum number of reacting particles are present and the number of effective collisions per second is at its greatest.

2 The curve is not as steep (has a lower gradient) at this point and the rate of the reaction is lower. Fewer reacting particles are present and so the number of effective collisions per second will be less.

3 The curve is horizontal (gradient is zero) and the reaction is complete. At least one of the reactants has been completely used up and so no further collisions can occur between the two reactants.

QUESTION SPOTTER

▶ You will often be given a graph showing the change in rate during a reaction. You will be asked questions about *how* the rate changes and *why* it changes during the reaction.

Q1 For a chemical reaction to occur the reacting particles must collide. Why don't all collisions between the particles of the reactants lead to a chemical reaction?

Q2 The diagrams below show the activation energies of two different reactions A and B. Which reaction is likely to have the greater rate of reaction at a particular temperature?

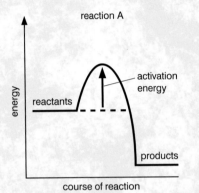

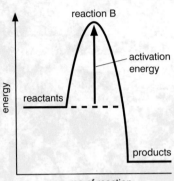

Q3 Look at the table of results obtained when dilute hydrochloric acid is added to marble chips.

Time (seconds)	0	10	20	30	40	50	60	70	80	90
Volume of gas (cm^3)	0	20	36	49	58	65	69	70	70	70

a What is the name of the gas produced in this reaction?

b Use the results to calculate the volume of gas produced:

i in the first 10 seconds

ii between 10 and 20 seconds

iii between 20 and 30 seconds

iv between 80 and 90 seconds.

c Explain how your answers to part **b** show that the rate of reaction decreases as the reaction proceeds.

d Use collision theory to explain why the rate of reaction decreases as the reaction proceeds.

e In this experiment the rate of the reaction was followed by measuring the volume of gas produced every 10 seconds. What alternative measurement could have been used?

Answers are on page 171.

REVISION SESSION 2 — Controlling the rate of reaction

☐ What can change the rate of a reaction?

■ There are six key factors that can change the rate of a reaction:
  - **concentration** (of a solution)
  - **temperature**
  - **surface area** (of a solid)
  - a **catalyst**
  - **pressure** (of a gas)
  - **light**.

■ A simple **collision theory** can be used to explain how these factors affect the rate of a reaction. Two important parts of the theory are:

  1 The reacting particles must collide with each other.

  2 There must be sufficient energy in the collision to overcome the activation energy.

☐ Concentration

■ **Increasing the concentration** of a reactant will **increase the rate** of a reaction. When a piece of magnesium ribbon is added to a solution of hydrochloric acid, the following reaction occurs:

magnesium	+	hydrochloric acid	$\rightarrow$	magnesium chloride	+	hydrogen
$Mg(s)$	+	$2HCl(aq)$	$\rightarrow$	$MgCl_2(aq)$	+	$H_2(g)$

■ As the magnesium and acid come into contact, there is effervescence – 'fizzing', and hydrogen gas is given off. Two experiments were performed using the same length of magnesium ribbon, but different concentrations of acid. In experiment 1 the hydrochloric acid used was 2.0 mol dm^{-3}, in experiment 2 the acid was 0.5 mol dm^{-3}. The graph below shows the results of the two experiments.

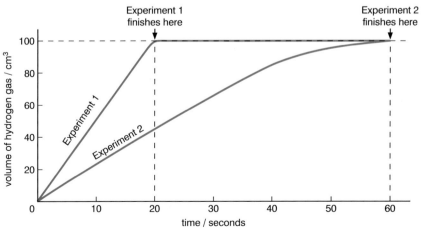

> **QUESTION SPOTTER**
>
> ▸ You are often asked to explain the differences in shapes of the graphs in experiments like these.
> ▸ You may also be asked to add further lines to a graph to represent what you would expect when conditions changed. (e.g. if the temperature was increased).

■ In experiment 1 the curve is steeper (has a greater gradient) than in experiment 2. In experiment 1 the reaction is complete after 20 seconds, whereas in experiment 2 it takes 60 seconds. The rate of the reaction is higher with 2.0 mol dm^{-3} hydrochloric acid than with

0.5 mol dm^{-3} hydrochloric acid. In the 2.0 mol dm^{-3} hydrochloric acid solution the hydrogen ions are more likely to collide with the surface of the magnesium ribbon than in the 0.5 mol dm^{-3} hydrochloric acid.

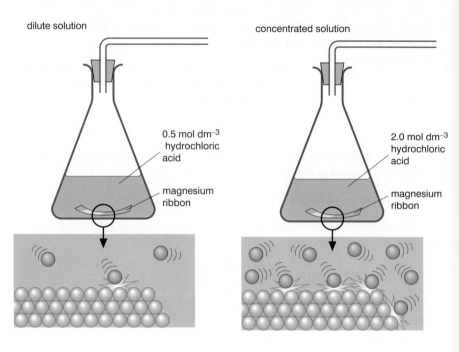

Temperature

- **Increasing the temperature** will **increase the rate** of reaction. Warming a chemical transfers kinetic energy to the chemical's particles. More kinetic energy means that the particles move faster. As they are moving faster there will be more collisions each second. The increased energy of the collisions also means that the proportion of collisions that are effective will increase.

- Increasing the temperature of a reaction such as that between calcium carbonate and hydrochloric acid will not increase the final amount of carbon dioxide produced. The **same amount** of gas will be produced in a **shorter time**.

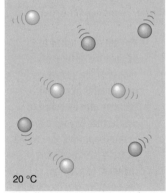

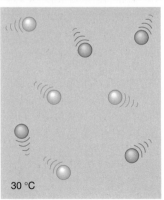

The rates of the two reactions are different but the final loss in mass is the same.

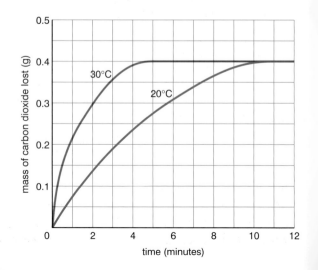

Surface area

- **Increasing the surface area** of a solid reactant will **increase the rate** of a reaction. The reaction can only take place if the reacting particles collide. This means that the reaction takes place at the surface of the solid. The particles within the solid cannot react until those on the surface have reacted and moved away.

- Powdered calcium carbonate has a much larger surface area than the same mass of marble chips. A lump of coal will burn slowly in the air whereas coal dust can react explosively.

QUESTION SPOTTER

▸ Questions often focus on the effects of concentration, temperature, surface area and catalysts on the rate of a reaction. You will usually be asked to *describe* and *explain* how the rate changes.

extra surface   even more extra surface

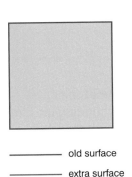

—— old surface
—— extra surface

On a large lump of marble, hydrochloric acid can only react with the outside surfaces. Breaking the lump into smaller pieces creates extra surfaces for the reaction.

Catalysts

- A **catalyst** is a substance that alters the rate of a chemical reaction without being used up itself. The mass of the catalyst remains unchanged throughout the reaction.

- Hydrogen peroxide decomposes slowly at room temperature into water and oxygen. This reaction is catalysed by manganese(IV) oxide.

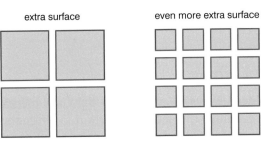

$$\text{hydrogen peroxide} \xrightarrow{\text{manganese (IV) oxide}} \text{water} + \text{oxygen}$$

$$2H_2O_2 \xrightarrow{MnO_2} 2H_2O + O_2$$

- Most catalysts work by providing an alternative 'route' for the reaction, lowering the activation energy 'barrier'. This increases the number of effective collisions each second.

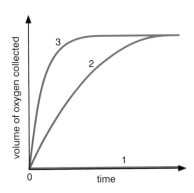

The manganese(IV) oxide has a dramatic effect on the rate of decomposition of hydrogen peroxide. The catalyst doesn't produce any extra oxygen but gives the same amount at a higher rate.
I = no catalyst
2 = one spatula measure
3 = two spatula measures

The catalyst provides a lower energy route from reactants to products.

- Some catalysts slow down reactions. These are called negative catalysts or **inhibitors**. Inhibitors are added to petrol to prevent 'pre-ignition' of the petrol vapour in the engine.

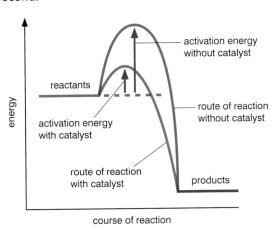

A* EXTRA

▸ Catalysts do not always increase the rate of a reaction. Most catalysts are positive catalysts (they increase the rate of a reaction) but inhibitors slow down reactions. Inhibitors are like negative catalysts — they act by increasing the activation energy of the reaction.

Pressure

- **Increasing the pressure** on a reaction between gases will **increase the rate** of the reaction. Increasing the pressure reduces the volume of the gas moving the particles closer together. If the particles are closer together there will be more collisions and therefore more effective collisions.

The same number of particles are closer together in a smaller volume. There will be more effective collisions each second.

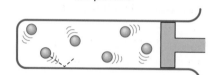 low pressure

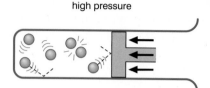 high pressure

Light

- **Increasing the intensity of light** will **increase the rate** of some reactions. This fact is important in photography. The photographic film is coated with chemicals that react when in contact with the light.

- Some laboratory chemicals, for example silver nitrate and hydrogen peroxide, are stored in brown glass bottles to reduce the effect of the light

CHECK YOURSELF QUESTIONS

Q1 Why does increasing the temperature increase the rate of a reaction?

Q2 The graph shows the results obtained in three different experiments. In each experiment marble chips were added to 50 cm^3 of 1 mol dm^{-3} hydrochloric acid (in excess) at room temperature. The same mass of marble was used each time but different sized chips were used in each experiment.

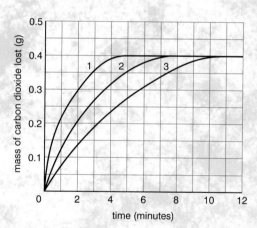

a i In which experiment was the reaction the fastest?
ii Give a reason for your answer.
b i Which experiment used the largest marble chips?
ii Give a reason for your answer.
c i How long did it take for the reaction in experiment 2 to finish?
ii Why did the reaction finish?
d Why was the same mass of carbon dioxide lost in each experiment?

e Experiment 3 was repeated at 50 °C rather than room temperature. How would the results be different from those shown for experiment 3?

Q3 a What is a catalyst?
b How does the catalyst affect the rate of a reaction?

Answers are on page 171.

Making use of enzymes

What are enzymes?

■ An **enzyme** is a biological catalyst. Enzymes are protein molecules that control many of the chemical reactions that occur in living cells. Enzymes are used in a wide range of manufacturing processes.

■ Increasing the temperature of a reaction will usually increase its rate. This is not the case in reactions where an enzyme is involved. The protein structure of an enzyme is affected by temperature. Above a certain temperature the protein becomes **denatured** and it will cease to function as a catalyst.

■ Enzymes are also sensitive to **pH**. Inside cells, most enzymes work best in neutral conditions, around pH 7. However, the enzymes in the stomach work best at about pH 2.

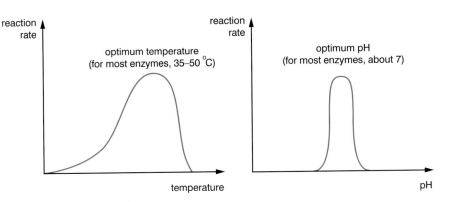

The effect of temperature and pH on the rate of a reaction involving enzymes.

How enzymes work

■ How enzymes work can best be understood by using a simple model. The enzyme provides a surface for the reaction to take place on. The surface of the enzyme molecule contains a cavity known as an **active site**. Reactant molecules become 'trapped' in the active site and so collide more frequently, resulting in more effective collisions and a greater rate of reaction.

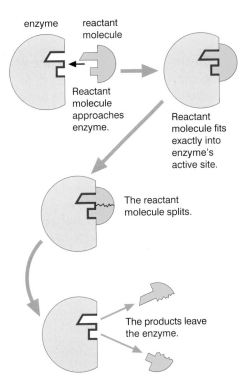

enzyme   reactant molecule

Reactant molecule approaches enzyme.

Reactant molecule fits exactly into enzyme's active site.

The reactant molecule splits.

The products leave the enzyme.

How enzymes catalyse reactions

> ### ⚡ A* EXTRA
>
> ▸ Enzymes are protein molecules with an active site where the reaction occurs. The active site has a certain shape and will only accommodate the shape of a particular molecule (sometimes referred to as the 'lock and key' model).
> ▸ This active site can be caused to lose its shape by changes in pH or temperature. If this happens it will no longer 'hold' the reacting molecule.

- This model also explains why enzymes cease to function above a certain temperature. The protein molecule is a long folded chain. As the temperature is increased the folded chain jostles and reforms and so the shape of the active site changes. Above a certain temperature the active site has changed so much that it is no longer able to 'trap' reactant molecules. Such an enzyme is said to be **denatured**.

⟦⟧ How are enzymes used in industry?

- Enzymes are used widely both in the home and industry.

The table shows some of the more important uses.

Process	Enzyme involved	Description
Brewing	Enzymes present in yeast	A mixture of sugar solution and yeast will produce ethanol (alcohol) and carbon dioxide. This process is called fermentation and is the basis of the beer and wine making industries.
Baking	Enzymes present in yeast	This also depends on the fermentation process. The carbon dioxide produced helps the bread dough rise. The ethanol evaporates during the baking process.
Washing using biological washing powders	Proteases and lipases	These enzymes break down proteins and fats found in stains (e.g. blood, egg) on clothing.
Making cheese	Lipases	These enzymes speed up the ripening of cheese.
Making baby foods	Proteases	These enzymes pre-digest the proteins in the food, so the baby can absorb them better
Making slimming foods	Isomerase	This enzyme converts glucose syrup into fructose syrup which tastes much sweeter, so less needs to be used in foodstuffs
Making sugar	Carbohydrase	Changes starch syrup into sugar syrup

- Industrial processes may use the **whole micro-organism** which contains the enzymes, for example yeast, or the **pure enzyme** extracted from the micro-organism, for example carbohydrase.

✦ IDEAS AND EVIDENCE

▸ Industry uses micro-organisms or pure enzymes as catalysts to bring about changes at normal temperatures and pressures. Their *advantages* are that they avoid the need for expensive equipment and also save on the use of energy for processes. The fact that they are also bio-degradable prevents environmental problems in their disposal.

▸ There are some *disadvantages* of using pure enzymes. They are expensive to produce and are wasteful because they cannot be recovered at the end of the process.

New areas of **enzyme technology** are based on making enzymes more efficient. This is done by:

1 **stabilising** the enzyme so that it can be kept working for a longer time,

2 **immobilising** it by trapping it in an inert solid support, e.g. as a coating for beads in a tower, so that it does not get 'lost' in the process.

Industry has two ways of using enzymes:

1 **Batch processing** – a 'one-off mixture' left for a length of time for the enzyme to produce the change required. The process is then stopped and the products removed, as in the use of biological detergents in a washing machine.

2 **Continuous processing** – the ingredients are continually passed through the enzyme (that is **stabilised** and **immobilised**) and the product continually collected, as in waste-water treatment.

Continuous processing is the **more efficient** of the two processes.

CHECK YOURSELF QUESTIONS

Q1 What is an enzyme?

Q2 In fermentation, glucose ($C_6H_{12}O_6$) is broken down to ethanol (C_2H_5OH) and carbon dioxide (CO_2).

  a What is used as a source of enzymes for this reaction?

  b Which two major industries make use of this reaction?

  c The optimum temperature for this reaction is about 40 °C. Why isn't a higher temperature used?

  d Write a word equation for the reaction.

  e Write a balanced symbol equation for the reaction.

Q3 **a** What is an active site?

  b Use the active site model to explain why enzymes usually only act as catalysts for one reaction.

Q4 **a** What are the advantages and disadvantages of using enzymes in industrial processes?

  b Why is continuous processing preferred to batch processing?

  c What is meant by 'stabilising' and 'immobilising' enzymes?

Answers are on page 172.

REVISION SESSION 1

Energy changes

⬚ Measuring energy transfers

■ In most reactions, energy is transferred to the surroundings and the temperature goes up. These reactions are **exothermic**. In a minority of cases, energy is absorbed from the surroundings as a reaction takes place and the temperature goes down. These reactions are **endothermic**.

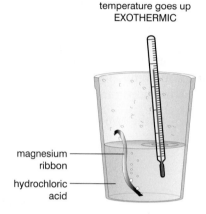

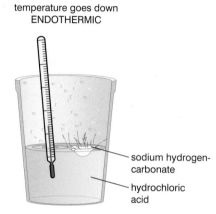

Energy transfers in a wide range of chemical reactions can be measured using a polystyrene cup as a calorimeter. If a lid is put on the cup, very little energy is transferred to the air and quite accurate results can be obtained.

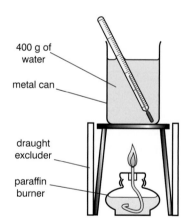

■ All reactions involving the combustion of fuels are exothermic. The energy transferred when a fuel burns can be measured using a **calorimetric technique**, as shown in the diagram on the left.

■ The rise in temperature of the water is a measure of the energy transferred to the water. This technique will not give a very accurate answer because much of the energy will be transferred to the surrounding air. Nevertheless, the technique can be used to compare the energy released by the same amounts of different fuels.

■ The energy change can be calculated using the equation:

Measuring the energy produced on burning a liquid fuel.

ΔH to the water	=	mass of water	×	specific heat capacity of water	×	rise in temperature of water
units in J or kJ		g or kg		$4.2J\ g^{-1}\ ^\circ C^{-1}$ or $4.2\ kJ\ kg^{-1}\ ^\circ C^{-1}$		$^\circ C$

Remembered as: $\Delta H = m \times SHC \times \Delta t$

☀ **QUESTION SPOTTER**

In calculation questions of this type, you will always be given the value of the SHC for water, i.e. $4.2J\ g^{-1}\ ^\circ C^{-1}$ or $4.2kJ\ kg^{-1}\ ^\circ C^{-1}$ However, you need to learn and remember the equation $\Delta H = m \times SHC \times \Delta t$

Units are important in this equation, that is, when you use g for mass of water, then ΔH is in J, but using kg for the mass gives ΔH in kJ.

Since $1\ cm^3$ of water weighs 1 g, the mass of water in the beaker is the same as the volume of water in cm^3.

WORKED EXAMPLE

2.0 g of paraffin were burned in a spirit burner under a metal can containing 400 cm^3 of water. The temperature of the water rose from 20 °C to 70 °C. Calculate the energy produced by the paraffin in J g^{-1} and kJ g^{-1}.

Equation:	ΔH	=	mass of water × 4.2 × temperature change
Substitute values:	ΔH	=	$400 \times 4.2 \times 50$
Calculate:	ΔH	=	84000 J per 2 g of paraffin
		=	42000 J g^{-1}
		=	42 kJ g^{-1}

⌂ Energy level diagrams and ΔH

- In Unit 9 Revision Session 1, the idea of activation energy was introduced using this diagram:

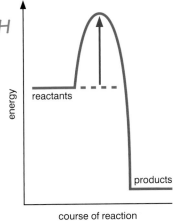

These are the more advanced form of basic **energy level diagrams**:

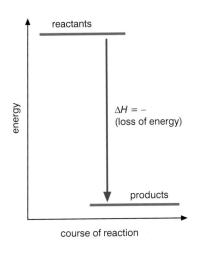

ΔH with a negative value

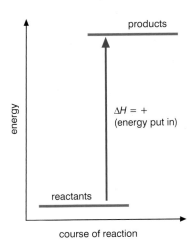

ΔH with a positive value

An **exothermic** reaction. Energy is being lost to the surroundings. ΔH is **negative**.

An **endothermic** reaction. Energy is being absorbed from the surroundings. ΔH is **positive**.

- All ΔH values should have a − or + sign in front of them to show if they are exothermic or endothermic.

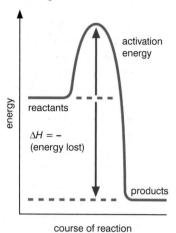

A full version of an energy level diagram

activation energy

energy

reactants

$\Delta H = -$ (energy lost)

products

course of reaction

■ The activation energy diagram can now be completed as shown left. The reaction for this diagram is exothermic, with ΔH negative.

Where does the energy come from?

■ When a fuel is burnt the reaction can be considered to take place in two stages. In the first stage the **covalent bonds** between the atoms in the fuel molecules and the oxygen molecules are **broken**. In the second stage the atoms combine and **new covalent bonds are formed**. For example, in the combustion of propane:

propane	+	oxygen	→	carbon dioxide	+	water
$C_3H_8(g)$	+	$5O_2(g)$	→	$3CO_2(g)$	+	$4H_2O(l)$

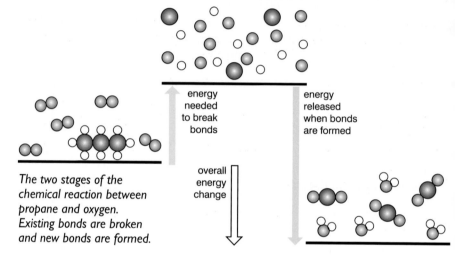

energy needed to break bonds

energy released when bonds are formed

overall energy change

The two stages of the chemical reaction between propane and oxygen. Existing bonds are broken and new bonds are formed.

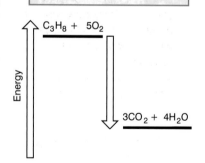

$C_3H_8 + 5O_2$

Energy

$3CO_2 + 4H_2O$

Stage 1: Energy is needed (absorbed from the surroundings) to break the bonds. This process is endothermic.

Stage 2: Energy is released (transferred to the surroundings) as the bonds form. This process is exothermic.

■ The overall reaction is exothermic because more energy is released when bonds are formed than is needed initially to break the bonds. A simplified **energy level diagram** showing the exothermic nature of the reaction is shown on the left.

■ The larger the alkane molecule, the more the energy that is released on combustion. This is because, although more bonds have to be broken in the first stage of the reaction, more bonds are formed in the second stage.

■ The increase in energy from one alkane to the next is almost constant, due to the extra CH_2 unit in the molecule.

In the table the energy released on combustion has been worked out per mole of alkane. In this way a comparison can be made when the same number of molecules of each alkane is burnt.

Alkane		Energy of combustion (kJ mol^{-1})
methane	CH_4	882
ethane	C_2H_6	1542
propane	C_3H_8	2202
butane	C_4H_{10}	2877
pentane	C_5H_{12}	3487
hexane	C_6H_{14}	4141

Bond energy calculations

■ Every covalent bond has a particular amount of energy needed to break it. This is the same as the amount of energy given out when it is made. This is the **bond energy** and its units are kJ mol^{-1}.

■ The table shows some values of bond energies.

bond	C–C	C–H	O=O	H–H	H–O	C=O	Cl–Cl	H–Cl
bond energy (kJ mol^{-1})	348	413	498	436	464	745	242	431

WORKED EXAMPLE

Calculate the energy change for the reaction between hydrogen and chlorine:

$$H_2 + Cl_2 \rightarrow 2HCl \qquad \text{i.e. } H\text{–}H + Cl\text{–}Cl \rightarrow 2 \times H\text{–}Cl$$

What does the sign of the energy change tell you about the reaction?

H–H	+	Cl–Cl	→	2	×	H–Cl
436 kJ mol^{-1}		242 kJ mol^{-1}		2	×	431 kJ mol^{-1}

total for bonds
= + 678 kJ mol^{-1}
(endothermic because bond breaking)

total for bonds
= – 862 kJ mol^{-1}
(exothermic because bond making)

Overall difference   – 862 kJ mol^{-1}
      + 678 kJ mol^{-1}
      – 184 kJ mol^{-1}

Answer: $\Delta H = -184$ kJ mol^{-1}
      It is an exothermic reaction (negative).

Summary of method:
1. Total all the bonds on the left and allocate a + sign.
2. Total all the bonds on the right and allocate a – sign.
3. Find the difference between the two values, not forgetting the sign (+ or –).
4. State if exothermic (–) or endothermic (+).

Q1 A 0.2 g strip of magnesium ribbon is added to 40 cm³ of hydrochloric acid in a polystyrene beaker. The temperature rises by 32°C. (The specific heat capacity of the hydrochloric acid can be assumed to be the same as that of water, i.e. 4.2 J g⁻¹ °C⁻¹.) Calculate

a the energy released in the reaction

b the energy released per gram of magnesium.

Q2 Calcium oxide reacts with water as shown in the equation:

$$CaO(s) + H_2O(l) \rightarrow Ca(OH)_2(s)$$

An energy level diagram for this reaction is shown below.

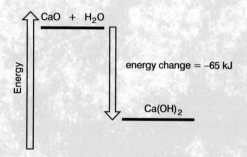

a What does the energy level diagram tell us about the type of energy change that takes place in this reaction?

b What does the energy level diagram indicate about the amounts of energy required to break bonds and form new bonds in this reaction?

Q3 Chlorine (Cl_2) and hydrogen (H_2) react together to make hydrogen chloride (HCl). The equation can be written as:

$$H–H + Cl–Cl \rightarrow H–Cl + H–Cl$$

When this reaction occurs, energy is transferred to the surroundings. Explain this in terms of the energy transfer processes taking place when bonds are broken and when bonds are made.

Q4 **a** Calculate the energy change for the combustion of methane (CH_4) in oxygen (O_2).

$$
\begin{array}{c}
\quad\; H \\
\quad\; | \\
H-C-H + 2 \times O{=}O \\
\quad\; | \\
\quad\; H
\end{array}
$$

$$\rightarrow O{=}C{=}O + 2 \times H–O–H$$

Use the bond energy values in the text.

b What does the sign of the energy change tell you about the reaction?

Answers are on page 173.

Chemical equilibria

Types of reversible reaction

■ Carbon burns in oxygen to form carbon dioxide:

carbon	+	oxygen	$\rightarrow$	carbon dioxide
C(s)	+	$O_2(g)$	$\rightarrow$	$CO_2(g)$

Carbon dioxide cannot be changed back into carbon and oxygen. The reaction cannot be reversed.

■ When blue copper(II) sulphate crystals are heated, a white powder is formed (anhydrous copper(II) sulphate) and water is lost as steam. If water is added to this white powder, blue copper(II) sulphate is re-formed. The reaction is **reversible**:

copper(II) sulphate crystals	$\rightleftharpoons$	anhydrous copper(II) sulphate	+	water
$CuSO_4.5H_2O(s)$	$\rightleftharpoons$	$CuSO_4(s)$	+	$5H_2O(l)$

When copper(II) sulphate crystals are heated they turn from blue to white.

The reaction can then be reversed by adding water.

■ A reversible reaction can go from left to right or from right to left – notice the double-headed '$\rightleftharpoons$' arrow used when writing these equations.

■ Another reversible reaction is the reaction between ethene and water to make ethanol. This is one of the reactions used industrially to make ethanol:

ethene	+	water	$\rightleftharpoons$	ethanol
$C_2H_4(g)$	+	$H_2O(g)$	$\rightleftharpoons$	$C_2H_5OH(g)$

When ethene and water are heated in the presence of a catalyst in a sealed container, ethanol is produced.

■ As the ethene and water are used up, the rate of the forward reaction decreases. As the amount of ethanol increases the rate of the back reaction (the decomposition of ethanol) increases. Eventually the rate of formation of ethanol will exactly equal the rate of decomposition of ethanol. The amounts of ethene, water and ethanol will be constant. The reaction is said to be in **equilibrium**.

⚡ A* EXTRA

▶ A chemical equilibrium is an example of a dynamic equilibrium (a moving equilibrium). Reactants are constantly forming products, and products are constantly reforming the reactants. Equilibrium is reached when the rates of the forward and backward reactions are the same.

⌷ Changing the position of equilibrium

■ Reversible reactions can be a nuisance to an industrial chemist. You want to make a particular product but as soon as it forms it starts to change back into the reactants! Fortunately scientists have found ways of increasing the amount of product that can be obtained (the **yield**) in a reversible reaction by moving the position of balance to favour the products rather than the reactants.

■ The position of equilibrium or yield can be changed in the following ways:
  • changing **concentrations**
  • changing **pressure**
  • changing **temperature**.

■ In the following example:

$$A(g) + 2B(g) \rightleftharpoons 2C(g) \qquad \Delta H = +$$

The yield of C is *increased* by:

1 adding more A and B ⎱ **concentration**
  removing C   ⎰

2 increasing the **pressure** because there are 3 molecules on the left (high pressure) but only 2 molecules on the right (low pressure)

3 increasing the **temperature** because the reaction is endothermic (ΔH is +).

■ A **catalyst** increases the rate at which the equilibrium is achieved. It does not change the yield because it does not affect the position of the equilibrium.

⌷ The Haber process

■ Ammonia is used to make nitrogen-containing fertilisers.

■ It is manufactured in the **Haber process** from nitrogen and hydrogen. The conditions include an iron catalyst, a temperature of 450 °C and 200 times atmospheric pressure.

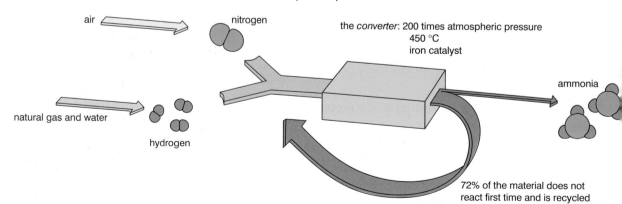

The Haber Process for making ammonia. The reactants have to be recycled to increase the amount of ammonia produced.

nitrogen	+	hydrogen	⇌	ammonia	
$N_2(g)$	+	$3H_2(g)$	⇌	$2NH_3(g)$	$\Delta H = -92 \text{ kJ mol}^{-1}$

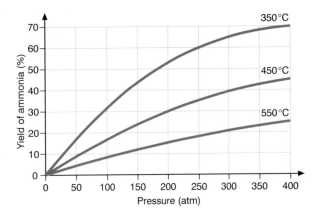

Effect of temperature and pressure on yield of ammonia

- The greatest yield of ammonia would be made using a low temperature (it is exothermic) but this would be slow. The temperature used of 450°C is a compromise since not so much is made, but it is produced faster. The iron catalyst is used to increase the rate also – it does not increase the yield. High pressure increases the yield and also the rate.

- The graph shows the effect of temperature and pressure on the yield of ammonia.

The contact process

- Sulphuric acid is a very important starting material in the chemical industry. It is used in the manufacture of many other chemicals, from fertilisers to plastics.

- It is manufactured in a process known as the **contact process** – sulphur dioxide is oxidised to sulphur trioxide.

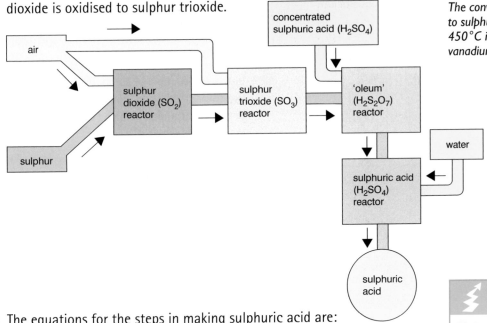

The conversion of sulphur dioxide to sulphur trioxide takes place at 450°C in the presence of a vanadium(V) oxide catalyst.

- The equations for the steps in making sulphuric acid are:

1	sulphur	+	oxygen	→ sulphur dioxide
	$S(s)$	+	$O_2(g)$	→ $SO_2(g)$
2	sulphur dioxide	+	oxygen	⇌ sulphur trioxide
	$2SO_2(g)$	+	$O_2(g)$	⇌ $2SO_3(g)$ $\Delta H = -192 \text{ kJ mol}^{-1}$
3	sulphur trioxide	+ sulphuric acid	→	'oleum'
		(concentrated)		
	$SO_3(g)$	+	$H_2SO_4(l)$	→ $H_2S_2O_7(l)$
4	'oleum'	+	water	→ sulphuric acid
	$H_2S_2O_7(l)$	+	$H_2O(l)$	→ $2H_2SO_4(l)$

⚡ A* EXTRA

▶ Low temperature often gives a good conversion of reactant into product but a very slow rate of reaction.

▶ The temperature chosen in an industrial process is often a compromise between one that favours the forward reaction (rather than the backward reaction) and one that gives a suitable rate of reaction.

■ It would seem simpler to make sulphuric acid by adding sulphur trioxide straight to water to avoid steps 3 and 4:

$$H_2O(l) + SO_3(g) \rightarrow H_2SO_4(l)$$

This is dangerous because the reaction is very exothermic and an 'acid mist' is made.

■ Step 2 above is the reaction of the contact process. The greatest yield of sulphur trioxide would be made at a low temperature (the reaction is exothermic), but this would be slow, so the compromise temperature of 450 °C is used — less is made but in a shorter time. High pressure would make more SO_3 but the equipment required would be costly. A catalyst increases the rate but not the yield.

CHECK YOURSELF QUESTIONS

Q1 When a chemical reaction is in equilibrium what does this mean?

Q2 What effect does a catalyst have on:
 a the rate of reaction
 b the yield of a reaction?

Q3 In the Haber process for making ammonia the forward reaction is favoured by a low temperature. Why is a temperature as high as 450°C used?

Q4 In the production of sulphuric acid, why is the sulphur trioxide from the contact process not added straight to water to make sulphuric acid?

Answers are on page 174.

UNIT 11: ORGANIC CHEMISTRY

REVISION SESSION 1 ▬▬ Hydrocarbons ▬▬

☐ What is organic chemistry?

- Originally, chemists thought that all **carbon compounds** could only come from living things - plants and animals - so, to describe them, they used the term **'organic'**, meaning 'of a plant or animal'.

- The first carbon compounds that chemists isolated were from **coal**, **crude oil**, **wood** and **animals**.

- Carbon compounds were then made from materials of non-living origin, but the term 'organic chemistry' continued to be used for all compounds based on carbon. Now, **'carbon chemistry'** is commonly used in textbooks as an alternative to 'organic chemistry'.

☐ More on the hydrocarbons called alkanes and alkenes

- Unit 5: Chemicals from oils, Revision Session 2, covered the basics on the hydrocarbons called alkanes and alkenes. These two families of hydrocarbons form two **homologous series**. Each member of a homologous series differs from the one before by one carbon atom. For example, in alkanes the group $-CH_2-$ is added to the chain.

- Alkanes and alkenes are all organic compounds and the information from Unit 5 is summarised below:

	Alkanes	Alkenes
General formula	$C_nH_{2n} + 2$	C_nH_{2n}
Description	saturated (no double C=C bond)	unsaturated (contains a double C=C bond)
Combustion	burn in oxygen to form CO_2 and H_2O (CO if low supply of oxygen)	burn in oxygen to form CO_2 and H_2O (CO if low supply of oxygen)
Reactivity	low	high (because of double C=C bond) undergo addition reactions
Chemical test	none	turn bromine water from brown to colourless (an addition reaction)
Uses	fuels	fuels making polymers (addition reactions)

▶ You will often be given a table of information about several fuels. The table will contain information about 'cost/g' and 'kJ/g' of energy produced, and whether it produces any pollutants e.g. soot (carbon). The question will ask you for:
- the best fuel 'economically', meaning 'cost/kJ', and
- the best fuel 'environmentally', meaning the one with the least impact on the environment.

▶ The question expects you to understand the issue of 'fuels', both economically and environmentally – recognising the ongoing problem about global warming.

⚡ A* EXTRA

▶ Organic compounds commonly contain nitrogen and chlorine – this is especially the case with plastics/polymers.

▶ When these compounds are burnt in a limited supply of air (e.g. to dispose of them), they produce hydrogen chloride, HCl, and hydrogen cyanide, HCN. Both of these are poisonous pollutants, and you need to make the link between these two gases and the presence of nitrogen and chlorine in the original molecule as a source of environmental pollution.

✦ IDEAS AND EVIDENCE

▶ The use of hydrocarbons (alkanes and alkenes) as fuels causes an increase in the carbon dioxide, CO_2, in the atmosphere and so to the greenhouse effect, leading to global warming.

▶ Since all carbon compounds burn to produce carbon dioxide, CO_2, the issue is a global problem.
- A 'good fuel' is cost-effective, which means that the price of the fuel compares well with the energy produced when burnt – 'low cost coupled with high amount of energy per kilogram'.
- A 'good fuel' is a 'clean fuel' – the products of combustion do not damage the environment.

■ Another addition reaction of alkenes is adding hydrogen (in the presence of a catalyst) to make an alkane:

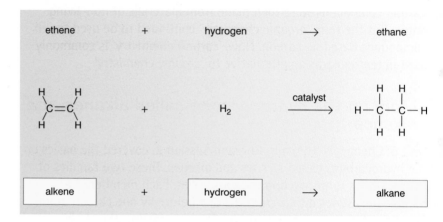

■ This reaction is used to make **margarine**. Vegetable oils contain unsaturated fats (i.e. fats with C=C double bonds). When hydrogen is added to these fats they become saturated and **harder**, so producing margarine.

Margarine is made of olive oil whose unsaturated molecules have been saturated with hydrogen.

🔲 What is isomerism?

■ The names of hydrocarbons are based on the position of the carbon atoms in their molecules. This is the structure of butane (C_4H_{10}):

$$H-\overset{\overset{\displaystyle H}{|}}{\underset{\underset{\displaystyle H}{|}}{C}}-\overset{\overset{\displaystyle H}{|}}{\underset{\underset{\displaystyle H}{|}}{C}}-\overset{\overset{\displaystyle H}{|}}{\underset{\underset{\displaystyle H}{|}}{C}}-\overset{\overset{\displaystyle H}{|}}{\underset{\underset{\displaystyle H}{|}}{C}}-H$$

The carbon atoms in a hydrocarbon molecule can be arranged in different ways. For example, in butane, C_4H_{10}, the carbon atoms can be positioned in two ways, while retaining the same molecular formula:

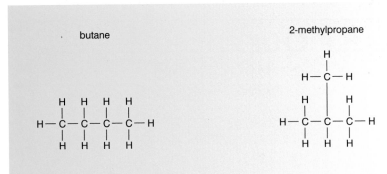

2-Methylpropane is a **structural isomer** (same atoms but rearranged) of butane which has a longer chain of carbons. This feature of alkane structure is called **structural isomerism**.

Alkenes show the same property, depending on the position of the double C=C bond. For example, alternatives of butene (C_4H_8) structure are:

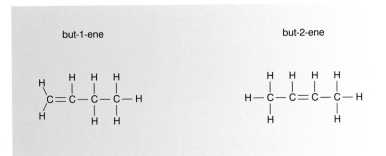

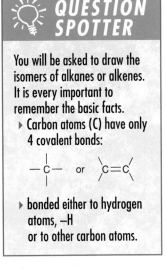

QUESTION SPOTTER

You will be asked to draw the isomers of alkanes or alkenes. It is every important to remember the basic facts.
▸ Carbon atoms (C) have only 4 covalent bonds:

bonded either to hydrogen atoms, –H or to other carbon atoms.

Each carbon atom has four bonds linked to either H atoms or other C atoms by single or double bonds.

The table shows isomers of the alkane C_5H_{12}.

Isomer	Pentane	2-Methylbutane	2,2-Dimethylpropane
Structure			
Boiling point (°C)	36	27	11

■ The boiling points *decrease* as the carbon chain gets *shorter*. This is because **intermolecular forces** between the molecules decrease as the carbon chain gets shorter (see polymers in Unit 5, Revision Session 2).

CHECK YOURSELF QUESTIONS

Q1 What is meant by each of the following?
a homologous series
b structural isomerism.

Q2 Draw two isomers of each of the following hydrocarbons:
a hexane, C_6H_{14}
b butene, C_4H_8

Q3 Why do isomers have different boiling points?

Answers are on page 174.

REVISION SESSION 2 ■ Alcohols and carboxylic acids ■

⌷ What are alcohols?

■ Alcohols are molecules containing the **–OH functional group** which is responsible for their properties and reactions.

■ Alcohols have the general formula $C_nH_{2n+1}OH$ and belong to the same homologous series, part of which is shown below.

Alcohol	Formula	Structure	Boiling point/°C
Methanol	CH_3OH	H—C—OH (with H above, below, and to left)	65
Ethanol	C_2H_5OH	H—C—C—OH	76
Propanol	C_3H_7OH	H—C—C—C—OH	97

■ Alcohols form structural isomers depending on where the –OH group is placed on the carbon chain. For example:

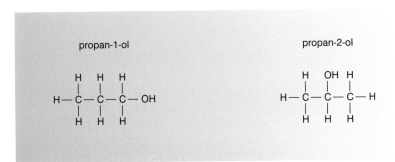

propan-1-ol

propan-2-ol

Ethanol – the commonest alcohol

- Ethanol, commonly just called 'alcohol', is the most widely used of the alcohol family. The major uses of ethanol are given below:

Use of ethanol	Reason
Alcoholic drinks, e.g. wine, beer, spirits	Affects the brain. It is a depressant, so releases inhibitions. Poisonous in large quantities.
Solvent, e.g. perfumes	The –OH group allows it to dissolve in water, and it dissolves other organic compounds
Fuel, e.g. for cars	It only releases CO_2 and H_2O into the environment, not other pollutant gases as from petrol. It is a renewable resource because it comes from plants, e.g. sugar beet, sugar cane.

- Ethanol is made by the process of **fermentation**.

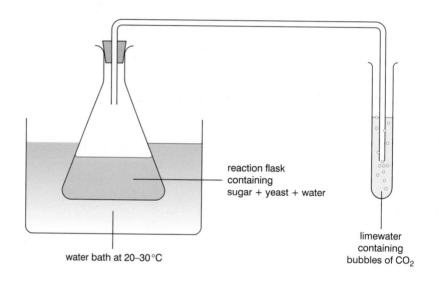

Fermentation apparatus.

- The chemical reaction for fermentation is:

$$\text{sugar} \xrightarrow{\text{yeast}} \text{ethanol} + \text{carbon dioxide}$$

$$C_6H_{12}O_6 \xrightarrow{\text{yeast}} 2C_2H_5OH + CO_2$$

- The **source** of the sugar determines the type of alcoholic drink produced, for example, grapes for wine, hops for beer.

- At the end of the fermentation process, which takes time because it is an enzymic reaction (yeast) and a batch process (see Unit 9, Revision Session 3), pure alcohol is extracted by **fractional distillation**. The mixture is boiled and the alcohol vapour reaches the top of the fractionating column where it condenses back to a liquid.

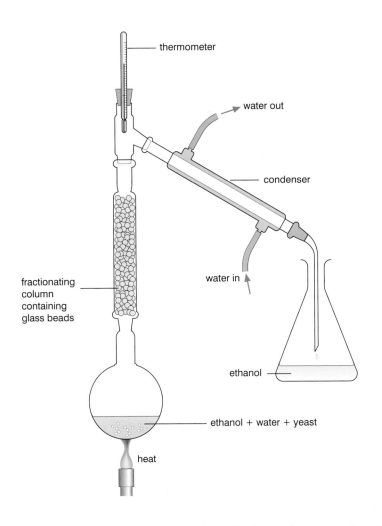

thermometer

water out

condenser

water in

fractionating
column
containing
glass beads

ethanol

ethanol + water + yeast

heat

*Apparatus for fractional distillation
of alcohol.*

QUESTION SPOTTER

The laboratory fermentation process is a very common question topic. As well as being able to draw and label the apparatus (as shown on page page 114), you should be able to explain why 20–30 °C is used: a higher temperature denatures the enzymes and they do not work.

■ On an **industrial scale**, ethanol is made from alkenes produced by the refining of crude oil. The reaction is:

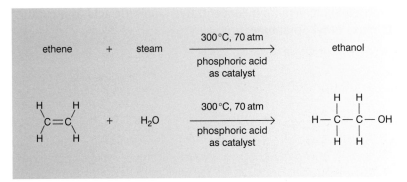

ethene + steam $\xrightarrow[\text{phosphoric acid as catalyst}]{300°C, 70 \text{ atm}}$ ethanol

$$\underset{\substack{H \\ | \\ H}}{\overset{\substack{H \\ | \\ H}}{C=C}} + H_2O \xrightarrow[\text{phosphoric acid as catalyst}]{300°C, 70 \text{ atm}} H-\underset{\substack{| \\ H}}{\overset{\substack{H \\ |}}{C}}-\underset{\substack{| \\ H}}{\overset{\substack{H \\ |}}{C}}-OH$$

■ These are quite extreme conditions in terms of energy (300 °C) and specialist plant equipment (to generate 70 atmospheres), and so the cost is high.

■ This process has the advantages over fermentation of being a continuous process and of producing ethanol at a fast rate.

▸ The formation of ethanol brings together ideas from various parts of the GCSE syllabus Unit 5 Oil, Unit 9 Enzymes and Unit 10 Energy.
▸ This topic will often be tested using 'extended written answers' and you will be expected to use correct terminology and to be logical in your use of English and the sequence in which you present the evidence for the making of ethanol.
▸ Remember that there are no 'rights and wrongs' – there are only 'advantages and disadvantages', since both of the methods described above continue to be used worldwide.

⚙ QUESTION SPOTTER

▸ You need to learn the three reactions of ethanol, to make sodium ethanoate, ethyl ethanoate and ethanoic acid, which are very commonly asked for in examination questions.
▸ Questions are likely to ask about the accidental oxidation of ethanol in the production of alcoholic drinks, which makes them taste of vinegar and so spoils the drinks. This is a particularly important topic to look for in examination questions.

IDEAS AND EVIDENCE

▸ The two methods of making ethanol are used to contrast traditional methods (fermentation) with more modern large-scale industrial methods (ethene and steam).

	Advantage	Disadvantage
Fermentation	Uses renewable resources. Flavour of ethanol for alcoholic drinks.	Slow 'batch' process. Only small amount of ethanol produced.
Ethene + steam	Fast 'continuous processes'. Large amounts of ethanol produced.	Uses non-renewable resource. Flavours have to be added artificially for drinks.

⌗ What are the reactions of ethanol (and other alcohols)?

■ The reason why ethanol is such an important chemical compound (as are other alcohols) is that it can be converted into other important compounds.

■ Ethanol reacts in the following ways because of the –OH functional group:

1 With sodium to give hydrogen gas:

$$\text{sodium} + \text{ethanol} \rightarrow \text{sodium ethanoate} + \text{hydrogen}$$
$$2Na(s) + 2C_2H_5OH(l) \rightarrow 2C_2H_5ONa(s) + H_2(g)$$

2 With ethanoic acid (and concentrated sulphuric acid as a catalyst) to make ethyl ethanoate:

Ethyl ethanoate belongs to a family called esters which have pleasant smells and are used as fragrances.

3   Ethanol can be oxidised to make ethanoic acid (a carboxylic acid):

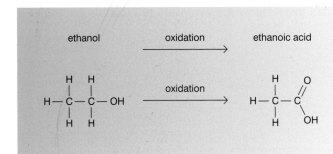

■ Ethanoic acid is the acid in vinegar. If wine or beer are not properly sealed, the ethanol is oxidised over time by the oxygen in the air and the wine or beer becomes acidic, so spoiling their taste.

What are carboxylic acids?

■ Carboxylic acids make up a homologous series of compounds containing the functional group –COOH.

Acid	Formula	Structure
methanoic acid	HCOOH	
ethanoic acid	CH₃COOH	
propanoic acid	C₂H₅COOH	

■ Carboxylic acids are used in industry and found in nature:

methanoic acid	The acid that ants can make and use to attack other insects, or for defence.
ethanoic acid	The main constituent of vinegar which is used as a preservative and flavouring. It is also used to make the fibre called acetate rayon.
citric acid	Found in fruits like oranges, lemons and limes. It is added to soft drinks to give them their sharp taste.
ascorbic acid	Known as vitamin C. It is found in citrus fruits like oranges, lemons and limes, as well as some fresh fruits. It is essential for human health.
salicylic acid	This is aspirin and is used for pain relief and to prevent heart attacks.

⌑ What are the reactions of carboxylic acids?

■ Carboxylic acids can be made by the oxidation of alcohols. Examples are shown:

■ These are the reactions of carboxylic acids:

1   **Esters** are made by reaction with alcohols (with concentrated sulphuric acid as a catalyst):

2   **Salts** are made by reactions with alkalis, carbonates and hydrogencarbonates:

ethanoic acid + sodium carbonate $\longrightarrow$ sodium ethanoate + water + carbon dioxide

$$2H-\underset{\underset{H}{|}}{\overset{\overset{H}{|}}{C}}-\overset{\overset{O}{\parallel}}{C}_{OH} + Na_2CO_3 \longrightarrow 2H-\underset{\underset{H}{|}}{\overset{\overset{H}{|}}{C}}-\overset{\overset{O}{\parallel}}{C}_{ONa} + H_2O + CO_2$$

ethanoic acid + sodium hydrogen-carbonate $\longrightarrow$ sodium ethanoate + water + carbon dioxide

$$H-\underset{\underset{H}{|}}{\overset{\overset{H}{|}}{C}}-\overset{\overset{O}{\parallel}}{C}_{OH} + NaHCO_3 \longrightarrow H-\underset{\underset{H}{|}}{\overset{\overset{H}{|}}{C}}-\overset{\overset{O}{\parallel}}{C}_{ONa} + H_2O + CO_2$$

- The reaction of carboxylic acids with carbonates and hydrogencarbonates to form carbon dioxide is used as a **chemical test** to identify the acids.

- Carboxylic acids are **weak acids** because they only partially dissociate into ions (see Unit 7):

$$CH_3COOH \rightleftharpoons CH_3COO^- + H^+$$

QUESTION SPOTTER

▸ You need to remember that carboxylic acids are *weak acids*. This means that questions on them involve work from other parts of the specification including Unit 7.
▸ Their acidity is the reason why they react to form *salts*, and they can be *tested* using UI paper (pH 4–6) or a carbonate or hydrogencarbonate to form CO_2 (turns limewater cloudy/milky).

? CHECK YOURSELF QUESTIONS

Q1 In the laboratory fermentation experiment to make ethanol from sugar using yeast, why is it important that
a the reaction is kept at 20–30°C and not higher than that temperature range?
b oxygen from the air cannot enter the reaction flask?

Q2 Give the structural formula of two isomers of butanol, C_4H_7OH.

Q3 What is 'esterification'?

Q4 How would you test an unknown liquid to show it is a solution of a carboxylic acid?

Answers are on page 175.

UNIT 12: AQUEOUS CHEMISTRY

Hardness of water

☐ What is hard water and what are its causes?

- Unit 6, Revision Session 3, covers the global roles of seas and oceans in the water cycle, and includes water purification.

- Unit 6, Revision Session 2, covers pollutants that dissolve in the water in the atmosphere, causing environmental damage due to acid rain.

- Before rainwater finally reaches reservoirs (for storage and treatment to purify it), it has fallen on the ground and compounds from rocks have dissolved in it. Certain dissolved compounds cause **hardness** in water.

- Rainwater is **weakly acidic** because of dissolved carbon dioxide in it:

weakly acidic rainwater

water +	carbon dioxide	→	carbonic acid

$$H_2O(l) + CO_2(g) \rightarrow H_2CO_3(aq)$$

- If rainwater falls on areas of land made of **calcium carbonate**, for example on **limestone** or **chalk**, a chemical reaction takes place:

Limestone dissolves as it reacts with acidic rainwater.

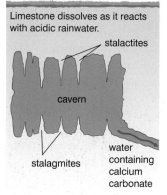

stalactites

cavern

stalagmites

water containing calcium carbonate

Reaction of rainwater with limestone.

carbonic acid	+	calcium carbonate (insoluble)	→	calcium hydrogen-carbonate (soluble)

$$H_2CO_3(aq) + CaCO_3(s) \rightarrow Ca(HCO_3)_2(aq)$$

- This reaction dissolves limestone and chalk rocks, and is the cause of **underground caverns** in limestone regions.

- The caverns often contain **stalactites** and **stalagmites** because the reaction above is reversible. As the dilute calcium hydrogencarbonate solution falls through the caverns, it loses carbon dioxide:

$$Ca(HCO_3)_2(aq) \rightarrow CaCO_3(s) + H_2O(l) + CO_2(g)$$

- Over thousands of years the tiny particles of insoluble calcium carbonate build up, forming the stalactites and stalagmites.

- In the same way, rocks containing **magnesium carbonate** will react with the weakly acidic rainwater, producing magnesium hydrogencarbonate, $Mg(HCO_3)_2$, which again dissolves in the water. In areas made of **gypsum** (calcium sulphate, $CaSO_4$), the rainwater dissolves the slightly soluble **calcium sulphate**.

- The result of these dissolving processes is that water can contain calcium hydrogencarbonate, magnesium hydrogencarbonate and calcium sulphate.

- **Hard water** is caused by the presence of the ions Ca^{2+} and Mg^{2+}. Water without these ions is called **soft water**.

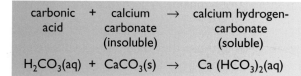

☼ QUESTION SPOTTER

- ▸ Although only a small part of the topic, the formation of stalactites and stalagmites is often examined. This is because their formation involves the reversible reaction of the calcium hydrogencarbonate/calcium carbonate which leads to hardness in water.
- ▸ Ensure that you learn this equation. The state symbols in the equation are essential if you are to fully explain the formation of solid stalactites and stalagmites.

Testing for hardness

- If a **scum** is formed when **soap solution** is added to water, then the water is **hard**. The scum is the **insoluble** salt **calcium stearate**.

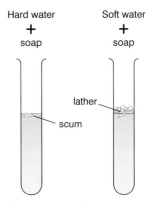

Hard water + soap   Soft water + soap

| calcium sulphate | + | sodium stearate (soap) | → | calcium stearate (scum) | + | sodium sulphate |

lather

scum

The reaction of soap and water is used to test water hardness.

- The same reaction takes place with magnesium compounds to form a scum of magnesium stearate.

- Once the soap has removed all the Ca^{2+} and Mg^{2+} ions from the water into the scum, the water is **soft** and a lather forms.

- The reaction of soap with water to form a lather is the basis for **testing degrees of hardness**. Soft water will give a lather with only one or two drops of soap solution – the more drops of soap needed, the harder the water is.

Types of hardness

- There are two types of hardness of water.

  1   **Temporary hardness** is caused by dissolved salt calcium hydrogencarbonate. When the water is heated, for example when boiled in a kettle, the salt breaks up to form insoluble calcium carbonate:

| calcium hydrogencarbonate | → | calcium carbonate | + | water | + | carbon dioxide |
| $Ca(HCO_3)_2$ (aq) | → | $CaCO_3(s)$ | + | $H_2O(l)$ | + | $CO_2(g)$ |

- The water is **softened**, but the calcium carbonate forms a scale in kettles and blocks up boilers and water pipes.

Calcium carbonate builds up on the heating elements inside kettles and washing machines.

- **'Permanent' hardness** is caused by dissolved **calcium sulphate** and cannot be softened by boiling.

Softening hard water

- **Boiling** removes only temporary hardness, when it deposits a scale of insoluble calcium carbonate.

- **Distillation** gives soft water from both temporary and permanent hard water because the solids are left behind in the heated flask.

Distilling soft water from hard water requires a lot of energy.

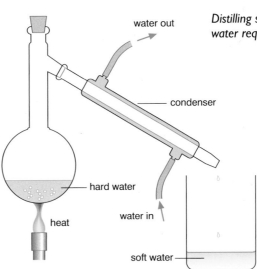

water out

condenser

hard water

water in

heat

soft water

▶ You need to be able to link calcium hydrogencarbonate, magnesium hydrogen-carbonate and calcium sulphate to the types of hardness they cause (temporary and 'permanent').

▶ More importantly, you must recognise that not all the equations for the reactions of these three compounds are quoted in this Unit – either for their role in causing hardness or for how they are removed.

▶ You need to go through the text and write the equations relating to all of these compounds using the guidance in the text, e.g. 'A similar reaction occurs for magnesium carbonate.'

■ Both methods are expensive because of the energy required.

■ Adding sodium carbonate - **washing soda, Na_2CO_3** - will remove both temporary and 'permanent' hardness by precipitating and the Ca^{2+} and Mg^{2+} ions. The reaction for calcium carbonate is:

sodium carbonate	+	calcium sulphate	→	calcium carbonate	+	sodium sulphate
$Na_2CO_3(aq)$	+	$CaSO_4(aq)$	→	$CaCO_3(s)$	+	$Na_2SO_4(aq)$

■ A similar reaction occurs for magnesium carbonate. Bath salts commonly contain sodium carbonate.

■ Passing water through **ion exchange resin** removes both types of hardness.

■ Over time, the resin loses all its Na^+ ions and is full of Ca^{2+} and Mg^{2+} ions. Concentrated sodium chloride solution is then poured through the resin, putting Na^+ ions back into it – this is called **regeneration** of the resin.

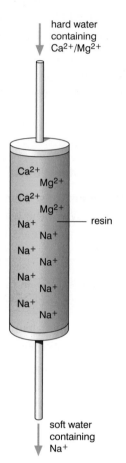

hard water containing Ca^{2+}/Mg^{2+}

resin

soft water containing Na^+

An ion exchange column

□ Hardness – good or bad?

■ Hard water has advantages as well as the disadvantages mentioned so far.

☼ **QUESTION SPOTTER**

▶ The two most commonly asked questions about softening hard water relate to washing soda and ion exchange resins.

▶ You need to learn the equations using washing soda (Na_2CO_3). But also learn the state symbols because this is an example of:

soluble + soluble → insoluble + soluble
salt   salt   salt   salt

▶ Ion exchange resin is the modern technique and is asked about more than washing soda.
Remember:
Remove Ca^{2+}/Mg^{2+}
with Na^+
When 'full' of Ca^{2+}/Mg^{2+}
regenerate Na^+

	Advantages	Disadvantages
hard water	Tastes better. Calcium is good for bones and teeth. The scale in pipes and boilers helps stop corrosion. Fewer heart attacks in hard water areas.	More soap used, leaves a scum and makes laundering more difficult. Scale in pipes and boilers makes them less efficient and they get blocked up eventually.
soft water	Clothes are cleaner and less soap is used. No scale in pipes and boilers. No scum when washing.	Soft water dissolves metal pipes, so putting metals such as lead (poisonous) into drinking water. More Na^+ ions in it – sodium is linked to heart disease.

Q1 a How are stalactites and stalagmites formed in caverns in limestone areas? Your answer should include all appropriate balanced chemical equations.

Number of drops of soap solution to give a lather			
	Sample A	Sample B	Sample C
untreated water	15	2	8
after boiling	13	2	3

Q2 The table shows the results of tests on three samples of water from different areas of the country.

a Which is a soft water sample?

b What compound is dissolved in Sample A? Explain the reason for your choice of answer.

c What compound is dissolved in Sample C? Explain the reason for your choice of answer.

d Write an equation for the formation of scum when soap is added to hard water.

Q3 Hard water can be softened in a variety of ways.

a Explain why distillation is not used on an industrial scale.

b Write the chemical equation (including state symbols) for the reaction of washing soda with calcium sulphate.

c Explain how ion exchange resins work, and how they are regenerated.

d Give **two** disadvantages of soft water.

Answers are on page 175.

Solubility – water as a solvent for gases and liquids

Dissolving gases in water

- In Revision Session 1 of this Unit, you met the idea of carbon dioxide dissolving in rainwater. Another example of carbon dioxide dissolving in water is in the manufacture of fizzy drinks. The bubbles seen when a bottle of fizzy drink is opened is carbon dioxide gas escaping from the water. Carbon dioxide, under pressure, was dissolved in the drink when it was manufactured.

- Oxygen also dissolves in water, and this is an essential process since fish and other aquatic creatures 'breathe' oxygen to maintain life, just as land animals and human beings do from the air.

- The unit used to describe the **solubility of a gas** in water is **g dissolved per 100 g of water** (see next page).

- The main factors that affect the solubility of a gas are **temperature** and **pressure**. The **colder** the water is, the **more gas** that will dissolve in it, as the table below shows:

Gas	Solubility (g of gas/100 g water)			
	0 °C	20 °C	50 °C	100 °C
carbon dioxide, CO_2	0.34	0.17	0.03	0.00
oxygen, O_2	0.007	0.005	0.003	0.00

- Increasing the temperature makes dissolved gases come out of water. Here are some common examples:

  - When water is heated, the first bubbles seen are dissolved oxygen and carbon dioxide coming out of the hot water (see table above).

  - In hot weather, fizzy drinks quickly go 'flat' as the carbon dioxide escapes more quickly than in cold weather.

  - When a fish aquarium gets too hot, the dissolved oxygen comes out of solution and the fish can die of oxygen starvation.

Pressure (atmospheres)	0	2	4	6	8	10
Solubility of oxygen (g of gas/100 g water)	0.0	0.015	0.028	0.04	0.056	0.069

- As an example of dissolved gas coming out of water, when you unscrew the top of a bottle of fizzy drink you see bubbles streaming upwards and hear the hiss of escaping gas. The drink inside the bottle has been under pressure; opening it decreases the pressure and the carbon dioxide escapes.

QUESTION SPOTTER

▸ You need to be clear about the conditions in which gases dissolve best in water – cold water temperature and high pressure.

▸ This topic is often examined in written questions using practical examples, e.g. fizzy drinks, and you need to relate the conditions to the example given.

Dissolving solids in water

- Throughout this book there are examples of solutions of solids (solutes) dissolved in water (solvent). They include acids and alkalis. It is worthwhile also remembering that ionic solids dissolve in water, while covalently bonded solids generally do not dissolve in water.

- Temperature conditions for **dissolving solids in water** are opposite to those for gases – generally, at **higher** temperatures, **more solid** can be dissolved in water.

- The unit used to describe the **solubility of a solid** is the same as for gases, namely g dissolved per 100 g of water.

- This unit is linked to temperature. For example, at 25 °C the solubility of potassium nitrate is 50 g/100 g water. This means the potassium nitrate solution is saturated – that is, no more than 50 g will dissolve in the 100 g of water. If more solid is added to the solution it will just sink to the bottom.

- If the saturated solution is cooled, then solid will come out of solution and be deposited on the bottom of the beaker.

- A **solubility curve** is used to show how solubility of a solid changes with temperature.

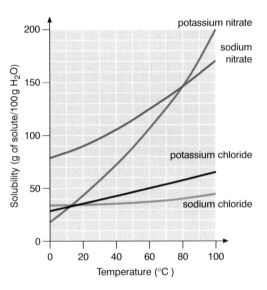

Solubility curves for four salts

QUESTION SPOTTER

You are expected to answer questions on solubility curves.
▸ Reading off the lines is straightforward
For example:
How many grams of sodium nitrate will dissolve in 100 g water at 60 °C?
Answer 125 g.
At what temperature will 100 g water dissolve 50 g of potassium chloride?
Answer 60 °C.

⚡ A* EXTRA

▸ A 'higher demand' question requires you to understand that these curves are about saturated solutions, so cooling them down means solid deposits out.
For example:
How many grams of sodium nitrate will be deposited if 100 g of its saturated solution is cooled from 100 °C to 40 °C?
Answer. At 100 °C:
170 g/100 g
At 40 °C: 105 g/100 g
170 − 105 = 65 g

CHECK YOURSELF QUESTIONS

Q1 Explain the following:
  a Bubbles are seen when a beaker of water is heated before it starts to boil.
  b A bottle of fizzy drink will go flat if the top is left off.

Q2 a What is meant by an 'unsaturated' solution?
  b How can you tell if a solution is 'saturated'?

Q3 Use the solubility curves above to answer the following questions:
  a What is the solubility of sodium chloride at 80 °C in g/100 g H₂O?
  b At what temperature would 100 g water dissolve 125 g potassium nitrate?
  c A saturated solution of potassium chloride is cooled from 100 °C to 60 °C. What mass of the salt is deposited?

Answers are on page 176.

REVISION SESSION 1

Techniques used in the laboratory

⌑ Safety in the laboratory

■ It is of the **highest importance** that you **work safely** when performing experiments in a chemistry laboratory. These are precautions you should follow:

- Wear **suitable clothing**, e.g. a laboratory coat or other protective clothing.

- Wear **safety goggles** to protect eyes.

- Wear **gloves** to protect hands.

- Perform experiments in a **fume cupboard**.

■ To work safely with chemicals, it is important to know what dangers they pose. Containers for chemical substances have **hazard symbols** to show what the dangers are. A substance may have more than one symbol.

Hazard symbol	Hazard	Explanation
	corrosive	Attacks and destroys living tissue, e.g. skin, eyes
	toxic	Can cause death when swallowed, breathed in or absorbed through the skin
	oxidising	Provides oxygen which allows other substances to burn far more fiercely
	harmful	Similar to toxic substances but less dangerous
	irritant	not corrosive but can cause reddening or blistering of the skin
	highly flammable	Catches fire easily

Identifying gases

■ Many chemical reactions produce a **gas** as one of the products. Identifying the gas is often a step in identifying the **compound** that produced it in the reaction (see 'Testing for anions' on pages 129 and 130.)

Gas	Formula	Test	Result of test
hydrogen	H_2	Put in a lighted splint (a flame)	'Pop' or 'squeaky pop' heard (flame usually goes out)
oxygen	O_2	Put in a glowing splint	Splint relights, producing a flame
carbon dioxide	CO_2	Pass gas through limewater	Limewater goes cloudy/milky
chlorine	Cl_2	Put in a piece of damp blue litmus paper	Paper goes red then white (decolourised)
ammonia	NH_3	Put in a piece of damp red litmus or UI paper	Paper goes blue

⚡ **A* EXTRA**

The chemical tests for gases are based on their chemical properties, and you can explain these using knowledge from other Units:

▸ Hydrogen: a 'squeaky pop' is a small explosion because oxygen has become mixed with the hydrogen. $2H_2 + O_2 \rightarrow 2H_2O$

▸ Oxygen: 'relights' is because oxygen must be present for the combustion process.

▸ Carbon dioxide: cloudiness is insoluble calcium carbonate (Unit 8). If carbon dioxide continues to be passed through, the cloudiness disappears – $CaCO_3(s)$ is changed to soluble calcium hydrogencarbonate, $Ca(HCO_3)_2$ (Unit 8).

▸ Chlorine: the gas is acidic, but also a bleaching agent (Unit 4).

▸ Ammonia: the only basic gas at GCSE or AS/A2 level (Unit 10).

Identifying metal ions (cations)

■ Ions of metals are **cations** – **positive ions** – and are found in ionic compounds. There are two ways of identifying metal cations:

• *either* from **solids** of the compound

• *or* from **solutions** of the compound.

Metal ions in solids

A. FLAME TESTS

■ In a flame test, a piece of nichrome wire is dipped into concentrated hydrochloric acid, then into the solid compound, and then into a **blue Bunsen flame**. A colour is seen in the flame which identifies the metal ion in the compound (see page 37).

Name of ion	Formula of ion	Colour seen in flame
lithium	Li^+	bright red
sodium	Na^+	golden yellow/orange
potassium	K^+	lilac (purple)
calcium	Ca^{2+}	brick red
barium	Ba^+	apple green

▶ If a solution gives a white precipitate with sodium hydroxide solution, it could contain Al^{3+}, Ca^{2+} or Mg^{2+}.

▶ Only Al^{3+} forms a precipitate that dissolves in excess sodium hydroxide solution – it can be identified by this.

▶ If a white precipitate does not dissolve, the solution has Ca^{2+} or Mg^{2+} in it. You can tell which one by performing a flame test on the solution – if a bright red flame is seen it is Ca^{2+}, if no red flame it is Mg^{2+}.

▶ You need to remember this identification process for Al^{3+}, Ca^{2+} and Mg^{2+} which is commonly asked in analysis questions.

⚡ A* EXTRA

▶ All the reactions with sodium hydroxide solution produce insoluble metal hydroxides: $Al(OH)_3(s)$, $Ca(OH)_2(s)$, $Cu(OH)_2(s)$, $Fe(OH)_2(s)$, $Fe(OH)_3(s)$, $Mg(OH)_3(s)$

▶ You need to be able to write the formula for these and their ions. Remember: copper and iron are transition metals so the roman numeral tells you the charge on the ion.

▶ The $Al(OH)_3$ dissolves in excess sodium hydroxide solution to form the soluble aluminate ion. This is a key reaction in the purification of bauxite which has to be done before electrolysis to produce aluminium (Unit 8, Revision Session 1, page 82).

▶ The green $Fe(OH)_2$ oxidises in air ($Fe^{2+} \rightarrow Fe^{3+}$) to form the reddish brown $Fe(OH)_3$.

Test for the ammonium ion, NH_4^+.

B. TESTS ON SOLUTIONS IN WATER

■ Metal ions are found in **ionic compounds**, so most will dissolve in water to form solutions. These **solutions** can be tested with other substances to identify the aqueous cation:

Name of ion in solution	Formula	Test	Result
aluminium	$Al^{3+}(aq)$	Add sodium hydroxide solution in drops. Keep adding until in excess	White precipitate formed which dissolves in excess sodium hydroxide solution
calcium	$Ca^{2+}(aq)$	Add sodium hydroxide solution in drops. Keep adding until in excess	White precipitate formed which remains even when excess sodium hydroxide solution added
copper(II)	$Cu^{2+}(aq)$	Add sodium hydroxide solution in drops	Light blue precipitate formed
iron(II)	$Fe^{2+}(aq)$	Add sodium hydroxide solution in drops	Green precipitate formed. On standing, changes to reddish brown colour
iron(III)	$Fe^{3+}(aq)$	Add sodium hydroxide solution in drops	Reddish brown precipitate formed
magnesium	$Mg^{2+}(aq)$	Add sodium hydroxide solution in drops. Keep adding until in excess	White precipitate formed which remains, even when excess sodium hydroxide solution is added

⬚ Identifying ammonium ions, NH_4^+

■ Ammonia gas is **very soluble** in water where it forms the ammonium ion and the hydroxide ion:

ammonia	+	water	→ ammonium ion	+	hydroxide ion
$NH_3(g)$	+	$H_2(l)$	→ $NH_4^+(aq)$	+	$OH^-(aq)$

This solution is alkaline, so when UI paper or red litmus paper is added to it, they both change to blue. This is not the test for ammonium ions – any alkaline solution will give this result.

■ The **test** for the **ammonium ion** is as in the diagram.

dilute sodium hydroxide solution

ammonium ion solution

damp red litmus paper

warm

blue if ammonia formed

Identifying anions

- As with metal cations, negative ions (anions) are tested as **solids** or as **solutions**.

TESTING FOR ANIONS IN SOLIDS

- The following test for anions in solids applies only to **carbonates**.

Dilute hydrochloric or sulphuric acid is added to the solid, and any gas produced is passed through limewater. If the limewater goes cloudy/milky, the solid contains a carbonate.

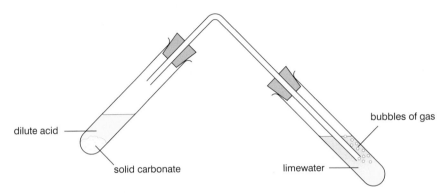

This reaction has been met before:

acid + carbonate → a salt + water + carbon dioxide

- There are two solid carbonates which have colour changes that can be used to identify them:

1   **Copper(II) carbonate** is a **green** solid which when heated goes **black** and gives off carbon dioxide:

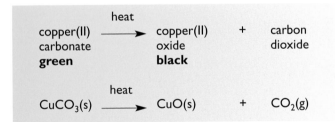

2   **Zinc carbonate** is a **white** solid which when heated goes yellow and gives off carbon dioxide.

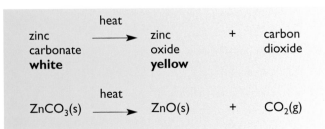

When cold, the zinc oxide changes from **yellow** back to **white**.

B. TESTING FOR ANIONS IN SOLUTION

- Ionic compounds are soluble in water, and so they form solutions that contain anions.

Name of ion	Formula	Test	Result
chloride	$Cl^-(aq)$	To a solution of the halide ions add: 1. dilute nitric acid 2. silver nitrate solution	white precipitate (of AgCl)
bromide	$Br^-(aq)$		green precipitate (of AgBr)
iodide	$I^-(aq)$		yellow precipitate (of AgI)
sulphate	SO_4^{2-}	Add: 1. dilute hydrochloric acid 2. barium chloride solution	white precipitate (of $BaSO_4$)
nitrate	NO_3^-	1. Add sodium hydroxide solution and warm 2. Add aluminium powder 3. Test any gas produced with damp red litmus paper	red litmus paper goes blue (ammonia gas is produced)

- If the silver halides – AgCl, AgBr and AgI – formed as in the table above are left to stand in daylight for a while, they go dark grey or black. This is because the light reduces them to silver. This darkening in light is the basis of photographic processes which use silver salts on camera film.

⚡ A* EXTRA

▸ The tests for the ammonium ion and the nitrate ion are interrelated and are usually combined to test for both at the same time, as shown on the right.

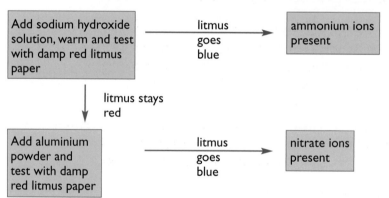

❓ CHECK YOURSELF QUESTIONS

Q1 The jar containing a chemical substance has two hazard labels on it showing it is both corrosive and highly flammable. What safety precautions should be taken when using this substance?

Q2 Describe the test for chlorine gas.

Q3 A solution is thought to contain the one of the cations aluminium, calcium or magnesium. Describe how you would identify which cation is present in the solution.

Q4 When a white powder is heated it changes in colour to yellow and gives off a gas. When cold, it becomes white again. Identify the white solid that is heated and the gas it gives off.

Answers are on page 177.

- The methods for identifying elements and compounds covered in Revision Session 1 are still used in school laboratories and have been used for at least a hundred years in the chemical industry as well.

- **Electronics** started with radio and television in the 1930s, and then **computers** were developed from the 1950s. Both were accelerated by the silicon chip and mass production. Chemists have used this electronics technology to develop new **techniques of analysis** – the process of identifying unknown substances and their composition.

- Modern instrumental methods have the **advantages** of being:

  - **accurate** - the composition of a sample can be found to a very high degree of accuracy. Errors are very low.

  - **sensitive** - very small samples can give accurate results.

  - **rapid** - using electronics and computer technology, the results of tests are produced very quickly.

- The ability to take a very **small sample** of material and analyse it in several minutes, or a few hours at the most, has had a huge impact on **monitoring**:

  - our **health** (medicine, e.g. blood tests),

  - the **environment** (e.g. levels of pollution by carbon monoxide).

- **Industrial processes** rely on these modern methods to ensure that the goods being produced are of a high quality (e.g. have no impurities). This is especially important in the **pharmaceuticals industry** (the manufacture of drugs and medical treatments).

- There are **disadvantages** as well, since some of these modern instruments are **expensive** to build and run. In addition, **specialist training** is needed to both operate them and analyse the results.

⊡ Identifying elements

Method	What it detects	How it works	Specific use	Advantages	Disadvantages
Flame photometry	Metal ions in solution	These are similar to flame tests. The sample is burnt and the light produced is analysed. The spectrograph shows lines which are then compared to patterns for known elements.	Aluminium salts are used to purify drinking water. Too high a level of aluminium ions can lead to poisoning. Constant monitoring is needed for health reasons.	Rapid sensitivity	Does not work as well for all metal ions. Cannot detect non-metal ions (anions).
Atomic absorption spectroscopy	Metal and non-metal ions in solution	Similar to above.	As above, but even more uses because it detects non-metal ions.	As above	Does not work as well for all metal and non-metal ions.

An atomic absorption spectrometer being used to analyse water samples to detect the presence of very small quantities of metals.

QUESTION SPOTTER

▸ You need to remember two of the techniques, e.g. flame photometry + atomic absorption spectroscopy, or a chromatographic method + mass spectrometry. This is because you are usually asked to name two techniques and then to give an advantage or disadvantage compared to one another.

▸ Remember the reason for using analytical instruments – accuracy, sensitivity, speed, use with small samples.

Identifying compounds

Method	What it detects	How it works	Specific use	Advantages	Disadvantages
Types of chromatography **1 Gas-liquid**	Separates gases in a mixture.	Similar to paper chromatography in that materials are separated according to how far each material travels in the equipment. Distances are compared to distances of known substances.	Pollution in the air, e.g. O_3/CO.	The range of chromatography techniques means they can be used on a wide range of gases, liquids and solids.	The measurements have to be compared against results for known and identified compounds.
2 Liquid-liquid	Separates small neutral molecules in solution.				
3 Ion exchange	Separates charged particles.		Medicine, e.g. analysis of components in blood and other body fluids.		
Mass spectrometry	Any element or compound.	Finds the M_r value of the compound/ element and the groups/atom each is made of.	As above	Detects elements as compounds. Results can be used to find the structure of an unknown compound.	Specialist training is needed to interpret the results fully.

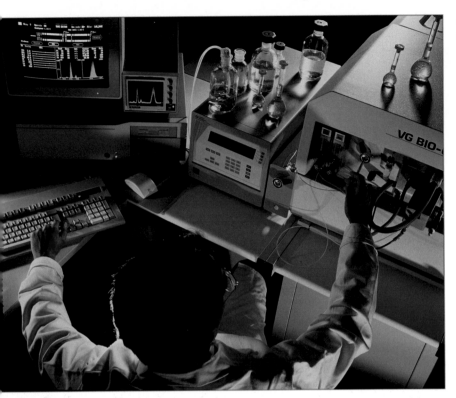

A mass spectrometer being used to analyse protein molecules.

⚡ A* EXTRA

▸ 'Higher demand' questions require you to explain how modern techniques were developed. Explain that present-day chemical analytical techniques were possible only because of the development of electronics and computers.

▸ You are likely to be asked for a specific purpose for modern analytical instruments, and a good example to remember is blood sampling from athletes in drug-testing programmes.

CHECK YOURSELF QUESTIONS

Q1 What are the advantages of using modern instrumental methods?

Q2 Name one instrumental method for identifying elements and one for identifying compounds. Give an advantage and a disadvantage of each of the two methods chosen.

Q3 Name two specific areas relating to health and the environment where instrumental methods are used for constant monitoring.

Answers are on page 177.

UNIT 14: EXAM PRACTICE

Exam tips

- **Read each question carefully**; this includes looking in detail at any **diagrams**, **graphs** or **tables**. Remember that any information you are given is there to help you to answer the question. Underline or circle the **key words** in the question and **make sure you answer the question that is being asked** rather than the one you wish had been asked!

- Make sure that you understand the meaning of the **'command words'** in the questions. For example:
  - **'Describe'** is used when you have to give the main feature(s) of, for example, a process or structure;
  - **'Explain'** is used when you have to give reasons, e.g. for some experimental results;
  - **'Suggest'** is used when there may be more than one possible answer, or when you will not have learnt the answer but have to use the knowledge you do have to come up with a sensible one;
  - **'Calculate'** means that you have to work out an answer in figures.

- Look at the **number of marks** allocated to each question and also the **space provided** to guide you as to the length of your answer. You need to make sure you include at least as many points in your answer as there are marks, and preferably more. If you really do need more space to answer than provided, then use the nearest available space, e.g. at the bottom of the page, making sure you write down which question you are answering. **Beware of continually writing too much because it probably means you are not really answering the questions.**

- Don't spend so long on some questions that you don't have time to finish the paper. You should spend approximately **one minute per mark**. If you are really stuck on a question, leave it, finish the rest of the paper and come back to it at the end. Even if you eventually have to guess at an answer, you stand a better chance of gaining some marks than if you leave it blank.

- In short-answer questions, or multiple-choice type questions, **don't write more than you are asked for**. In some exams, examiners apply the rule that they only mark the first part of the answer written if there is too much. This means that the later part of the answer will not be looked at. In other exams you would not gain any marks, even if the first part of your answer is correct, if you've written down something incorrect in the later part of your answer. This just shows that you haven't really understood the question or are guessing.

- **In calculations always show your working**. Even if your final answer is incorrect you may still gain some marks if part of your attempt is correct. If you just write down the final answer and it is incorrect, you will get no marks at all. Also in calculations you should write down your answers to as many **significant figures** as are used in the question. You may also lose marks if you don't use the correct **units**.

- In some questions, particularly short-answer questions, answers of only one or two words may be sufficient, but in longer questions you should aim to use **good English** and **scientific language** to make your answer as clear as possible.

- If it helps you to answer clearly, don't be afraid to also use **diagrams** or **flow charts** in your answers.

- When you've finished your exam, **check through** to make sure you've answered all the questions. Cover over your answers and read through the questions again and check that your answers are as good as you can make them.

I Bobby finds out about hydrogen peroxide.

a) Hydrogen peroxide has the formula H_2O_2.

   i) Write down the **names** of the two elements that make up hydrogen peroxide.

   hydrogen   and   oxygen ✔ ✔ _____ (2)

   ii) How many atoms are there all together in one molecule of hydrogen peroxide?

   4 ✔ _____ (1)

   (iii) Why is hydrogen peroxide called a compound?

   Atoms chemically joined. ✔ _____ (2)

b) Bobby heats hydrogen peroxide to 60 °C.
   Hydrogen peroxide breaks down into water and oxygen.

   i) Write the word equation for this chemical reaction.

   hydrogen peroxide → water + oxygen ✔ ✔ _____ (2)

   ii) Finish the sentence about the reaction by choosing the **best** word from this list.

   acid   **alkali**   **catalyst**   (**thermal**) ✔

   Heating hydrogen peroxide causes _____ decomposition. (1)

   iii) Bobby does a test to show that the gas given off is oxygen.
   Describe the test he does and the results of the test.

   Put in burning splint, it burns brighter. ✗ _____ (2)

c) Bobby does more experiments. He decomposes hydrogen peroxide under
   different conditions.
   The original experiment was carried out at 60 °C.
   Finish the table. For each of the changes made, write down whether
   the rate is **faster, slower** or **the same** as the original experiment. The first one
   has been done for you.

change made	the rate will be
add ice to the hydrogen peroxide	slower
heat the hydrogen peroxide to 90 °C	faster ✔
add some water at 60 °C	faster ✗
add some manganese (IV) oxide at 60 °C	faster ✔

(3)

⑨/13   (Total 13 marks)

⌷How to score full marks

a) i) Correct responses.

   ii) Correct answer.

   iii) This is a 2-mark question and the student has missed out on the second mark. The student should have spotted that the word 'compound' compared to 'mixture' implies 'hard to separate', 'constant composition' and 'atoms joined in simple ratio'. Any of these would have gained the second mark.

b) i) Correct equation. The student has picked up the 'clues' in the question and written the equation based on the information given.

   ii) Correct – the marker has accepted 'ringing' the answer instead of writing it on the line.

iii) The response is true but *not* the test for oxygen which is 're-lights a glowing splint'.

c) 'faster' is correct: increasing temperature increases rate.

   'faster' is wrong: 60 °C is the *same* temperature, so 'same' is the correct response.

   'faster' is correct: manganese(IV) oxide is the catalyst for this decomposition.

- A mark of 9 out of 13 represents a grade C on this Foundation Tier question.

---

2 a) Which one of the *ions* below is a cause of hard water?

Put a ring round your choice.

Al^{3+} Cu^{2+} (Mg^{2+}) ✓ Na^+ (1)

b) Two samples of water come from different parts of the country.
Describe how you would test them to find out which one was the harder water.

Add soap solution and shake to see which one gave a lather. ✓ (2)

c) Give **one** method of softening hard water.

Pass it through an ion exchange resin. ✓ (1)

③/4 (Total 4 marks)

⌷How to score full marks

a) The correct ion has been chosen.

b) The student has correctly given the soap solution ('and shake' is correct but not a mark point).

Both samples will give a lather if enough soap solution is added, but the student has not realised the need for 'drops' of soap solution – the one giving a lather with fewest drops will be the softer water.

c) The correct response has been given. There are other methods but ion exchange resins work on both types of hardness (temporary and permanent), so is the safest choice of method.

- A mark of 3 out of 4 corresponds to a grade C on this Foundation Tier question.

3 Use the periodic table to answer the following questions.

a) Give the symbol for an atom of iron.

Fe ✓ (1)

b) What is the atomic number of oxygen?

16 ✗ (1)

c) Name the **two** elements present in methane, CH_4.

1 carbon ✓

2 hydrogen ✓ (2)

d) Use elements from the box to answer the following questions.

calcium	**fluorine**	**helium**	**nitrogen**	**sodium**

i) Which element is in the same group as neon?

fluorine ✗ (1)

ii) Which **two** elements are in the same period?

1 fluorine ✓

2 nitrogen (1)

4/6 (Total 6 marks)

How to score full marks

a) Correct response.

b) 16 is the mass number (protons + neutrons). The correct answer is '8'. The student has mixed up the choice of numbers from the box in the periodic table.

c) Correct responses.

d) i) Fluorine is in the same *period* as neon, *not* the same group. The correct response is helium.

ii) Correct response.

- A mark of 4 out of 6 represents a grade C on this Foundation Tier question.

1 *To gain full marks in this question you should write your ideas in good English. Put them into a sensible order and use the correct scientific words.*

Some compounds react with water to produce acidic or alkaline solutions.

Explain the work of Arrhenius **and** of Brønsted-Lowry in developing the ideas about acids and bases.

(Total 4 marks)

2 This question is about a family of elements in the periodic table.
Find the elements **lithium, sodium** and **potassium** in a copy of the periodic table.

a) What is the number of the group that these elements are in? (1)

b) What name is given to this family of elements? (1)

c) Here is some information about these elements.

name	hardness	melting point in °C
lithium	fairly hard to cut with a knife	180
sodium	easy to cut with a knife	98
potassium	very easy to cut with a knife	64

i) Describe the trends in hardness and melting point going down the group from lithium to potassium. (2)

ii) **Rubidium** is the element below potassium in this group.
Which of the following is most likely to be the melting point of rubidium?
Put a ring around the correct answer.

O °C   **40 °C**   **100 °C** (1)

d) A lithium atom has three electrons around its nucleus.

i) Which diagram, **A, B** or **C**, shows the correct arrangement of these electrons?
Put a ring around the correct answer.

(1)

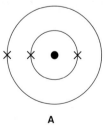

    A   **B**   **C**

ii) How is the arrangement of electrons in a sodium atom similar to that in a lithium atom?

Put a tick (✓) in the box next to the correct statement.

They both have the same total number of electrons. ☐

They both have the same number of filled electron shells. ☐

They both have the same number of electrons in the outer shell. ☐ (1)

e) Even before scientists knew about electrons and shells, sodium and potassium were put into the same group.
Suggest why. (1)

(Total 8 marks)

3 Use substances from the list to complete the table.

ammonia
carbon
carbon dioxide
ethanol
ethyl ethanoate
methanol

Each substance may be used once, more than once or not at all.

description	substance
a gas that turns damp red litmus paper blue	
a substance found in all alcoholic drinks	
an element	
a substance added to aqueous ethanol to make methylated spirit unfit to drink	
a sweet smelling substance used as a flavouring	
a substance produced by fermenting sugar	

(6)

(Total 6 marks)

Answers are on page 178.

1 a) The symbols for two *isotopes* of oxygen are:

$$^{16}_{8}O \qquad\qquad ^{18}_{8}O$$

i) Explain why they can be described as *isotopes* of oxygen.

(1)

ii) *same number of protons but different number of neutrons* ✓

The arrangements of electrons in energy levels (shells) for an oxygen atom is 2,6. Give the electron arrangements of an oxide ion.

2,8 ✓

(1)

iii) Give the chemical formula of potassium oxide.

KO_2 ✗

(1)

b) Using dot and cross symbols, complete the diagram to show how the outer electrons are arranged in a molecule of ammonia, NH_3.

(2)

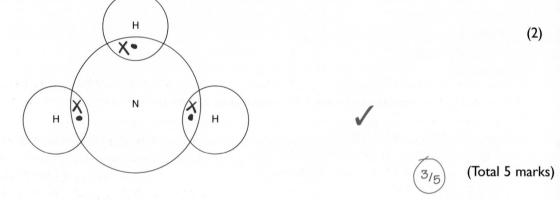

✓

③/5 (Total 5 marks)

🗂 How to score full marks

a) i) The student has given the correct response. Notice that both the number of protons *and* neutrons have to be given for the mark. You are expected to know the definition of 'isotopes'.

ii) The correct answer has been given since the oxide ion is O^{2-}, i.e. two extra electrons are added to complete the orbit/shell.

iii) The ions are K^+ and O^{2-} so the correct response is K_2O. The student has made a common mistake in the writing of a formula from ions.

b) The student has scored one mark for putting a pair of ×• in the overlap between N and H (a covalent bond-pair). The second mark has been missed because nitrogen is in group 5, so should have five electrons in its outer orbit/shell: the student has failed to put two more electrons on the circle around N.

• A mark of 3 out of 5 corresponds to a grade C on this Foundation / Higher Tier overlap question.

2 **a)** Nitrogen-based fertilisers are used to increase crop yields.

Calculate the percentage of nitrogen in the fertiliser ammonium sulphate, $(NH_4)_2SO_4$.

(Relative atomic masses: H = 1; N = 14; O = 16; S = 32)

$(NH_4)_2SO_4$ = 2 × 14 + 8 × 1 + 32 + 4 × 16 = 132 ✓

percentage N = $\frac{14}{132}$ × 100 = 10.6% ✗

(2)

b) *To gain full marks in this question you should write your ideas in good English. Put them into a sensible order and use the correct scientific words.*

Explain why the amount of fertiliser used is increasing, and describe the damage that fertilisers can cause to life in rivers and lakes.

The population of the world is increasing so there are more people. ✓

Fertilisers wash off the land into rivers and lakes and make plants and

weeds grow more. ✓

They take oxygen out of the water so the fish die. ✓

(4)

4/6 (Total 6 marks)

⬚ How to score full marks

a) The student has gained one mark for correctly calculating M_r of the compound. The error in the calculation was using 14 instead of 28, which is the mass of *all* the nitrogen in the compound. This is a common error: the student used A_r of nitrogen (14) instead of the total mass. The correct answer is 21.2%.

b) There are two issues to be addressed in this question:

1. increasing use of fertilisers

2. the damage they can cause

The mark scheme will allocate equal marks to both issues.

Issue 1. The student has scored one mark for 'increasing population' but 'more people' is just another way of saying the same thing and does not gain a mark. If the student had put 'increasing population so more food is needed' then two marks would have been given. The student could also have gained a second mark for 'more land is under cultivation' or 'better crop yields needed'.

Issue 2. The student has gained two marks for 'plants and weeds grow more' and 'fish die' (lack of oxygen).

A third mark was not given because plants do not remove oxygen from water; they increase oxygen levels (photosynthesis). This is a common misconception. The loss of oxygen is due to increased bacteria in the water produced by decaying plants.

The student has written the answer in a clear and logical way, so has not lost a mark for poor English or order of ideas. (Poor presentation would have meant the maximum mark a student could achieve would be 3 or 4 marks.)

- A mark of 4 out of 6 marks corresponds to a grade C on this Foundation / Higher Tier overlap question.

3 This question is about catalysts.

a) Explain what is meant by the term **catalyst**.

Something that speeds up the rate of a reaction. ✓ (2)

b) Catalyst **A** is added to 100 cm3 of hydrogen peroxide solution.

The experiment is repeated with catalysts **B** and **C**.

Each of the hydrogen peroxide solutions has the same concentration and a temperature of 25 °C.

The graph shows the results of this experiment.

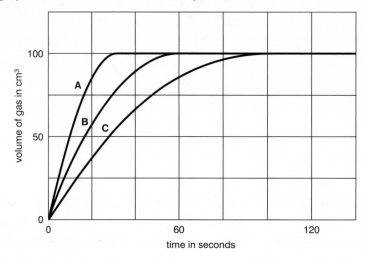

i) Which catalyst, **A**, **B** or **C**, produces 50 cm^3 of oxygen in 30 seconds?

_C_ ✓ (1)

ii) Which catalyst produces oxygen gas the fastest in the first 30 seconds?

_A_

Explain your choice.

The slope is steepest. ✓ (1)

iii) The final volume of oxygen collected in each experiment is the same.

Suggest why.

Concentration of hydrogen peroxide is same each time. ✓ ✓ (2)

iv) The experiment with catalyst A is repeated at 50 °C rather than 25 °C.

Oxygen is produced faster.

Explain why. Use ideas about particles in your answer.

Heat makes the particles move faster so there are more collisions and the reaction is faster. ✓ ✓ (2)

c) Yeast contains an enzyme.

i) What is the difference between an enzyme and a catalyst?

✗ _____ (1)

ii) Finish this word equation for the reaction that happens when yeast is added to sugar solution.

yeast

sugar ⟶ | ethanol ✓ | + | carbon dioxide ✓ | (2)

iii) The enzyme invertase can be injected into the centres of chocolates.

Suggest why this is done.

✗ _____ (1)

(9/12) Total 12 marks

How to score full marks

a) This is a 2-mark question and the student has only gained 1 mark. The second mark could have been given for adding 'unchanged in the reaction' or 'can be collected at the end of the reaction'.

b) i) Correct response by reading the graph correctly.

   ii) Correct answers.

   iii) Correct response, but the student has not spotted that this is a 2-mark question. '25 °C' needs to be given for the second mark.

   iv) Correct answer, showing a good understanding of the way increasing temperature affects the rate of a reaction.

c) i) Enzymes are 'biological' catalysts, and the student should have spotted this crucial difference instead of not attempting this part.

   ii) The student has correctly identified the process as 'fermentation'.

   iii) Invertase changes sucrose into fructose and glucose, so that the centre is 'sweeter' (1 mark) and turns 'liquid' (1 mark).

   • A mark of 9 out of 12 marks corresponds to a grade C on this Foundation / Higher Tier overlap question.

4 Before electronic flash units, photographers had to use flash bulbs to take photographs in dark conditions. The flash was produced by the reaction of very thin magnesium wires with oxygen to form the compound magnesium oxide.

a) Write the balanced equation for the reaction.

$Mg + O_2 \rightarrow MgO$ ✓✓✗

(3)

b) Explain why magnesium oxide is called a compound.

Two elements have combined together. ✓✓

(2)

c) Magnesium oxide is an ionic compound containing magnesium ions, Mg^{2+}, and oxide ions, O^{2-}.

i) The atomic number of magnesium is 12. Its mass number is 24.

Copy and complete the table.

	number of protons	number of neutrons	number of electrons
Mg	12 ✓	12 ✓	12 ✓
Mg^{2+}	12 ✓	12 ✓	14 ✗

(4)

ii) Suggest how the oxide ions, O^{2-}, were formed when the magnesium burned in oxygen. ✗

Oxygen molecules have gained 2 electrons. ✓

(2)

8/11

(Total 11 marks)

How to score full marks

a) The student has given the correct formulae for the reactants (1 mark) and product (1 mark). The equation, which should be $2Mg + O_2 \rightarrow 2MgO$, is not balanced correctly, so the third mark has been lost.

b) Both marks gained by correct response.

c) i) 5 boxes are correct, but the number of electrons for Mg^{2+} is '10' since 2 electrons have been lost to make the ion. (This question is marked as '4 marks but deduct one mark for each error'.)

ii) The error is 'molecules' – it should have been 'atoms'.

• A mark of 8/11 represents a 'good C grade' on this Foundation / Higher Tier overlap question.

1 Anita reads an article in a scientific magazine.

The article suggests a way to reduce the amount of carbon dioxide in the atmosphere.

The article begins:

'If forests are not removing enough carbon dioxide from the atmosphere, why not make an artificial forest instead?'

The article goes on to suggest a process:

1. Very large lakes of calcium hydroxide solution remove carbon dioxide and make a precipitate of calcium carbonate, $CaCO_3$.
2. The calcium carbonate is then heated to make calcium oxide, CaO, and carbon dioxide.
3. The carbon dioxide reacts with rocks to make an unreactive solid.
4. The calcium oxide from step 2 is added back to the lake to make calcium hydroxide, $Ca(OH)_2$.

a) Describe what you would see when carbon dioxide reacts with calcium hydroxide solution (limewater). (2)

b) i) Finish this equation for the effect of heat on calcium carbonate.

$CaCO_3 \rightarrow$ _____ + _____ (1)

ii) In this reaction, heat is used to split up the calcium carbonate.

What type of reaction is taking place? (1)

c) i) Write an equation for the reaction that takes place with the water when calcium oxide is added back to the lake. (2)

ii) This is an **exothermic** reaction.

Explain what this means. (1)

d) Joe also reads the article. He says that this process will not take carbon dioxide out of the atmosphere.

What evidence can Anita find in the article to convince Joe that he is wrong? (2)

e) Explain why scientists are trying to remove carbon dioxide from the atmosphere. (3)

(Total 12 marks)

2 Metals are used to conduct electricity.

a) Aluminium is used to make wires that carry electricity across the country. The aluminium wires have a steel core. They are suspended between pylons.

Suggest why a steel core is needed. (1)

b) Pure metals are often converted into alloys.

Why are alloys sometimes used instead of pure metals? (1)

c) Sir Harry Kroto was one of the discoverers of buckminsterfullerene. This is a form of carbon in which the molecules contain sixty carbon atoms arranged in the shape of a ball.

Metal atoms can be put inside the molecules of buckminsterfullerene. Under the right conditions, the product can conduct electricity.

Scientists hope to use this property of buckminsterfullerene to make tiny electronic components for computers. The computers could then be smaller and faster than those used today.

i) Suggest **two** ways in which Sir Harry Kroto could have informed other scientists of his work. (2)

ii) Suggest how other scientists could have confirmed that Sir Harry Kroto's ideas were correct. (1)

iii) Suggest a benefit to society from this discovery. (1)

d) When buckminsterfullerene is completely burnt in oxygen, a gas is formed.

i) Give the name of the gas. (1)

ii) State how this gas can be collected. (1)

(Total 8 marks)

3 The table gives information about three fuels that can be burned to heat a house.

Fuel	Heat produced (in kJ per gram)	Cost per gram in pence (p)	Products of burning	
			Soot from flame?	Solid left?
A	59	6	✓	✗
B	40	7	✗	✗
C	42	5	✓	✓

a) Use the data to calculate which fuel produces most heat per penny.
Show clearly how you worked out your answer. (2)

b) When burned, which fuel is the cleanest?

Explain your answer. (2)

c) Write the word equation for the **incomplete** combustion of methane.

methane + oxygen → ……………….. + ……………….. (2)

(Total 6 marks)

Answers are on pages 178–180.

1   Dolomite is a type of rock used for buildings and statues.

Dolomite contains calcium carbonate, $CaCO_3$ and magnesium carbonate, $MgCO_3$.

Magnesium carbonate reacts with sulphuric acid to release carbon dioxide.

$$MgCO_3 + H_2SO_4 \rightarrow MgSO_4 + H_2O + CO_2$$

a)   i)   Write a balanced equation for the reaction between calcium carbonate and sulphuric acid.

$\underline{CaCO_3 + H_2SO_4 \rightarrow CaSO_4 + H_2O + CO_2}$ ✔   (1)

ii)   How could you show that the gas produced in these reactions is carbon dioxide?

$\underline{pass\ it\ through\ limewater}$ ✔   (2)

b)   Acid rain contains sulphuric acid.

i)   Describe a problem that is likely to occur when acid rain falls on a statue made of dolomite.

$\underline{eaten\ away\ by\ reaction\ with\ the\ acid}$ ✔   (1)

ii)   Acid rain also reacts with metals.

Write a balanced equation for the reaction of sulphuric acid with zinc.

$\underline{Zn + H_2SO_4 \rightarrow ZnSO_4 + H_2}$ ✔✔   (2)

c)   4.2 g of magnesium carbonate is reacted with excess sulphuric acid.

Calculate the **mass** of carbon dioxide released in this reaction.

Use the equation to help you.

You must show how you work out your answer.

(Relative atomic masses: C = 12, O = 16, Mg = 24)

$\underline{MgCO_3 = 24 + 12 + 3 \times 16 = 84}$ ✔
$\underline{84g \longrightarrow 44g\ CO_2}$ ✔
$\underline{4.2g \longrightarrow 22g}$ ✘

mass of carbon dioxide = 22 g   (3)

d) This is an energy level diagram for the reaction between a carbonate and an acid.

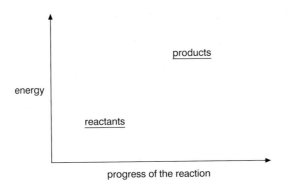

What does this diagram tell you about the reaction? (1)

exothermic ✗

⑦/10 (Total 10 marks)

☐ How to score full marks

a) i) The student has spotted that the two carbonates are similar (both of group 2 metals), so has just changed 'Mg' to 'Ca' in the equation given.

ii) This is the *test* (1 mark) but the *result* needs to be given also, i.e. 'turns milky/cloudy' (1 mark).

b) i) Correct response.

ii) Correct equation (1 mark for correct formulae, 1 mark for 'balance').

c) The student has made a good attempt at the calculation and gained marks for '84' and that 44g CO_2 is made from it. The 1/20 scaling factor is correct for 4.2 g, but the correct answer is 1/20 of 44 g, i.e. 2.2 g.

d) This is *endothermic* – energy needs to be put into the reactants to make the products.

• A score of 7/10 represents a grade C on this Higher Tier question.

9 The table gives some information about two metals **X** and **Y**.

	X	**Y**
melting point (°C)	63	1083
density (g per cm³)	0.9	8.9
appearance of ore used to extract metal	white solid	red solid
method of extraction of metal	electrolysis of molten salt	reduction of oxide ore with carbon
first extracted	during 1800s	thousands of years ago

a) i) Use the information in the table to answer the following questions.

Give one reason for suggesting that **X** is an alkali metal.

Low density ✔ (1)

ii) Give two reasons for suggesting that **Y** is a transition metal.

Ore is red. ✔ (2)

iii) Suggest why metal **X** was not extracted until long after metal **Y**.

Needs electricity which wasn't available until 1800s. ✔ (1)

b) The alkali metals lithium and potassium both react vigorously with water.

Describe one similarity and one difference that you would **see** if small samples of these metals were placed in separate beakers containing cold water.

Similarity _react with water_ ✗

Difference _flame colours_ ✔ (2)

4/6 (Total 6 marks)

⌂ How to score full marks

a) i) Correct answer. 'Low melting point' is equally acceptable for 1 mark.

ii) This is a 2-mark question – the student needed to also give *either* 'high melting point' *or* 'high density' for the second mark.

iii) Correct response.

b) The 'similarity' answer only restates what the question says already. The student needed to give 'float on water', 'more around on surface' or 'roll into a ball' for the mark.

The difference is correct. 'Potassium more reactive than lithium' is also correct.

• A score of 4/6 represents a C grade on this Higher Tier question.

3 a) The structures of diamond and graphite are shown below.

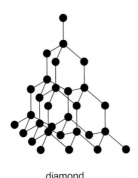
diamond

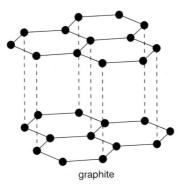
graphite

Use these structures to explain why:

i) both diamond and graphite have high melting and boiling points;

Both giant structures, so many covalent bonds to break. ✓ (1)

ii) diamond is harder than graphite;

Its structure is stronger than graphite. ✗ (2)

iii) graphite is used as a lubricant.

The layers can slide over each other because there are only weak bonds between them. ✓ ✓ (1)

b) State a property **not** mentioned above which graphite shares with metals.

Explain the cause of this property.

Conducts electricity because the layers can slide over each other and move. ✓ (2)

4/6 (Total 6 marks)

⌑ How to score full marks

a) i) The student has given the correct response.

ii) The response is not specific enough to gain the mark. The student should have mentioned that the diamond structure has 'each carbon linked to four others in a tetrahedral shape which makes the structure strong and rigid' or 'graphite has layers joined together by weak forces so it is not as hard'.

iii) This is a 2-mark question and the student has realised this by giving the reason why it is a lubricant ('layers can slide') and the cause of

the property ('weak bonds'), so gaining both marks for the correct answers.

b) 'Conducts electricity' is the correct property shared by graphite and metals, but the student has given the wrong explanation to gain the second mark. The correct reason is the presence of delocalised electrons which are free to move along the layers (*not* between the layers).

• A mark of 4/6 represents a grade B on this Higher Tier question.

I A possible new way to 'mine' metal ores, called phytomining, was developed in the later years of the 20th century.

Some plants absorb and concentrate metals when they are grown on soils rich in metal compounds. Metals can be extracted from these plants.

In California, the plant *Streptanthus polygaloides* can contain up to 1% of its dry mass as nickel. When the plant is burned, nickel oxide is produced.

a) Suggest why *Streptanthus polygaloides* is burned before transport to the extraction factory. (1)

b) i) What mass of nickel is contained in 1 tonne dry mass of *Streptanthus polygaloides*?
    Give your answer in kg.
    You must show how you work out your answer.
    (1 tonne = 1000 kg) (1)

ii) What is the maximum mass of nickel oxide, NiO, that could be obtained from this nickel?
    Give your answer in kg.
    You must show how you work out your answer.
    (Relative atomic masses: O = 16, Ni = 59)
    (1 tonne = 1000 kg) (3)

c) In the extraction process, nickel oxide is reduced to nickel.

The process is similar to the production of iron in a blast furnace.

In the blast furnace, the raw materials are iron ore, carbon and limestone.

Explain why limestone is needed in the production of iron but not needed in this production of nickel. (2)

d) Nickel is purified by electrolysis. This is very similar to the way that copper is purified.

Impure nickel is made the positive electrode (anode) and pure nickel the negative electrode (cathode).

Nickel leaves the positive electrode.

$$Ni \rightarrow Ni^{2+} + 2e^-$$

Nickel is deposited onto the negative electrode.

i) Complete this ionic equation for the reaction at the negative electrode.

Ni^{2+} _____ $\rightarrow$ _____ (1)

(ii) The mass lost by the positive electrode during the electrolysis is **more** than the mass of nickel deposited on the negative electrode.

Suggest why. (1)

e) Other metals that may be extracted by phytomining are platinum and gold.

Suggest what the metals that may be extracted in this way have in common.

Use a copy of the periodic table to help you. (1)

(Total 10 marks)

2 A student carried out a titration to find the concentration of phosphoric acid in a solution.

50.00 cm^3 of phosphoric acid solution was neutralised by 28.00 cm^3 of a sodium hydroxide solution of concentration 0.50 mol dm^{-3}.

The equation for the reaction is:

$$3NaOH(aq) + H_3PO_4(aq) \rightarrow Na_3PO_4(aq) + 3H_2O(l)$$

a) Calculate the number of moles of NaOH used. (2)

b) Calculate the concentration of the phosphoric acid in moles per cubic decimetre (mol dm^{-3}) (3)

(Total 5 marks)

3 a) The surface of aluminium metal is always covered with a thin layer of another substance.

i) Give the chemical name of the thin surface layer and state the effect it has on aluminium. (2)

ii) This thin surface layer can be made thicker by treating the aluminium using electrolysis, in which aluminium is made the anode.

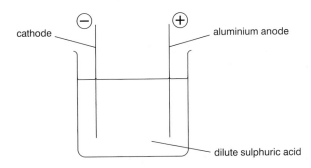

Give the name of this process. (1)

b) The sulphuric acid can be manufactured from sulphur by the following sequence of reactions.

$$\text{sulphur} \rightarrow \text{gas } \mathbf{X} \rightarrow \text{gas } \mathbf{Y} \rightarrow \text{sulphuric acid}$$

Gas **X** is converted into gas **Y** using air in the presence of the catalyst vanadium(V) oxide at 450 °C.

Give the name of gas **X**. (1)

c) Many metals are used in the form of mixtures called alloys.

Aluminium alloys are used to make aircraft.

Iron alloys such as stainless steel are used to make saucepans and cutlery.

i) State one advantage of aluminium alloys over pure aluminium. (1)

ii) State one reason why aluminium alloys are used to make aircraft. (1)

iii) State one advantage of stainless steel over iron. (1)

(Total 7 marks)

Answers are on pages 180–181.

ANSWERS

UNIT 1: ATOMIC STRUCTURE, BONDING AND PROPERTIES

1 Ideas about atoms and their structure (page 2)

Q1 People were not prepared to accept the idea of atoms because they were so small that they could not be seen.

Comment This is the reason why Democritus's theory was rejected at the time.

Q2 Any three from:
indivisible spheres/particles
atoms of same element are of identical/same mass
atoms of different elements have different masses
atoms join together to form compounds
all molecules of a compound contain same type and number of atoms.

Comment Dalton's theory needs to be learnt as 'key points'.

Q3 Atoms are not 'indivisible'. They are made of even smaller particles (protons, neutrons and electrons).

All atoms of the same element are not always identical, with the same mass. Most elements have isotopes, i.e. have atoms with same number of protons but a different number of neutrons, hence different masses.

Comment Atoms are made of subatomic particles and elements usually exist as isotopes.

2 How are atoms put together? (page 5)

Q1 a The atomic number is the number of protons in an atom. (It is equal to the number of electrons.)

Comment Always define atomic number in terms of protons. However, as atoms are neutral there will always be equal numbers of protons and electrons.

b The mass number is the total number of protons and neutrons in an atom.

Comment Remember that electrons have very little mass and so mass number cannot refer to electrons.

Q2

Si	14	14	14	2,8,4
Mg	12	14	12	2,8,2
S	16	16	16	2,8,6
Ar	18	22	18	2,8,8

Comment The top number is the mass number and the bottom (smaller) number is the atomic number. The difference between the two numbers is the number of neutrons.

Q3 a (i) C; (ii) B; (iii) C or E or F; (iv) B; (v) C

Comment To have no overall charge the number of protons (positive charges) must equal the number of electrons (negative charges).
The atomic number (number of protons) is unique to a particular element. It is the atomic number that defines the element's position in the periodic table.

b

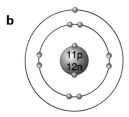

Comment Remember that an atomic diagram should show the number of protons and neutrons in the nucleus and the number and arrangement of electrons.

3 Chemical bonding (page 9)

Q1 a Covalent

   b covalent

   c ionic

   d covalent

   e ionic.

> **Comment** Remember that ionic bonding involves
> a metal and a non-metal; covalent bonding involves
> two or more non-metals. Hydrogen, chlorine,
> carbon, oxygen and bromine are non-metals.
> Only sodium and calcium in the list are metals.

Q2 a K^+

   b Al^{3+}

   c S^{2-}

   d F^-.

> **Comment** These can be worked out from the
> position of the element in the periodic table. Look
> back in the unit for the rule if you have forgotten
> it. You will always be given a periodic table in the
> exam. Get used to using it: it will help you to gain
> marks in the exam.

Q3 a

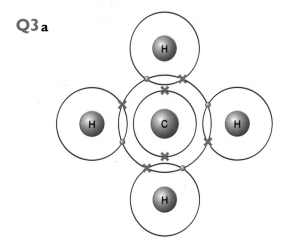

   b

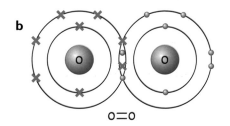

$O{=}O$

c

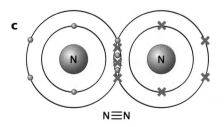

$N{\equiv}N$

d

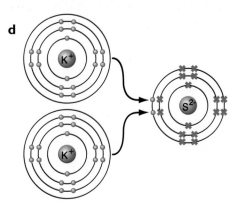

e

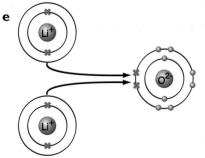

> **Comment**
> 1 Remember that covalent compounds contain
>   non-metals.
> 2 You can get the atomic number (needed to
>   work out the number of electrons) from the
>   periodic table.
> 3 With covalent compounds try drawing the
>   displayed formula first. You will need to work
>   out how many covalent bonds each atom can
>   form. Again, the periodic table will help you.
>   For example, oxygen is in Group 6 so it can
>   form two covalent bonds. Once you have
>   got the displayed formula, each bond
>   corresponds to a shared pair of electrons.
>   Don't forget the first electron shell can hold
>   2 electrons, others hold 8 electrons. So don't
>   miss any electrons out.
> 4 In examples of ionic bonding don't forget to
>   write the formulae of the ions that are formed.

States of matter (page 12)

Q1 Gas

Comment The particles are moving faster and are further apart.

Q2 The forces between atoms in the aluminium must be greater than those in sodium.

Comment More energy is needed to separate the aluminium particles.

Q3 When steam condenses to water it gives out a lot of energy.

Comment The steam contains the energy associated with a change of state.

Q4 There is no temperature change at a change of state because the energy is being used to separate the particles.

Comment This is the fundamental point about changes of state.

Q5 Condensing

Comment Gas to liquid is shown by the state symbols.

Structures and properties (page 15)

Q1 a Potassium chloride exists as a giant ionic lattice. There are very strong electrostatic forces holding the ions together. A considerable amount of energy is needed to overcome the forces of attraction so the melting point is high.

Comment The key ideas relating to melting point are: strong forces between particles; large amounts of energy needed to overcome these forces.

b Potassium chloride is ionically bonded. When molten or dissolved in water the ions are free to move and carry an electric current.

Comment Remember that an electrolyte allows an electric current to flow through it when molten or dissolved in water – not when in the solid state.

Q2 a The carbon atoms are held by strong covalent bonds within the hexagonal layers. This can give a structure great strength.

Comment Have a look at the diagram of the structure of graphite. Remember that covalent bonds are strong bonds.

b Only three out of the four of carbon's outer shell electrons are used in forming covalent bonds. Each atom has an electron which is only loosely held to the atom. When a voltage is applied these electrons move, forming an electric current.

Comment Graphite has a structure similar to that of metals – there is a 'cloud' of electrons which are free to move.

Q3 The bonds within the molecule are strong (the intramolecular bonds) but the bonds holding the methane molecules together are weak (intermolecular bonds). Therefore methane molecules require very little energy to be separated from each other.

Comment This is one of the ideas candidates find very confusing. Always try to be precise. There are bonds within a molecule as well as bonds between molecules. You wouldn't be expected to use 'intramolecular' and 'intermolecular', but if you do be sure to get them the right way round!

Q4 In graphite, electrons can only move along the layers of atoms (in one plane) but not between them. In metals, the electrons can move in any plane as the lattice is symmetrical in all directions.

Comment This is the fundamental difference between the conduction of electricity in metals and graphite. Both contain delocalised electrons, but graphite electrons can only move along the layers and not between them.

Q5 a C is a metal.

Comment Conducts as solid and liquid.

b A contains ionic bonds.

Comment Conducts when molten but not as solid.

c D has a giant covalent structure.

Comment Does not conduct electricity but has high melting and boiling points.

d B has a simple molecular structure.

Comment Does not conduct electricity but has low melting and boiling points.

UNIT 2: CHEMICAL FORMULAE AND EQUATIONS
1 How are chemical formulae written? (page 18)

Q1 a NaCl

Comment Na (group 1) combining power 1, Cl (group 7) combining power 1.

b MgF_2

Comment Mg (group 2) combining power 2, F (group 7) combining power 1. 2, 1, cross over = Mg1 F2 = MgF_2.

c AlN

Comment Al (group 3) combining power 3, N (group 5) combining power 3. 3, 3, cancel = Al1 N1 = AlN

d Li_2O

Comment Li (group 1) combining power 1, O (group 6) combining power 2.

e CO_2

Comment C (group 4) combining power 4, O (group 6) combining power 2. 4, 2, cancel = C1 O2 = CO_2.

Q2 a Fe_2O_3

Comment Fe combining power 3, O (group 6) combining power 2.

b PCl_5

Comment P combining power 5, Cl (group 7) combining power 1.

c $CrBr_3$

Comment Cr combining power 3, Br (group 7) combining power 1.

d SO_3

Comment S combining power 6, O (group 6) combining power 2. 6, 2, cancel = S1 O3 = SO_3.

e SO_2

Comment S combining power 4, O (group 6) combining power 2. 4, 2, cancel = S1 O2 = SO_2.

Q3 a K_2CO_3

Comment K combining power 1, CO_3 combining power 2.

b NH_4Cl

Comment NH_4 combining power 1, Cl (group 7) combining power 1.

c H_2SO_4

Comment H combining power 1, SO_4 combining power 2.

d $Mg(OH)_2$

Comment Mg (group 2) combining power 2, OH combining power 1. Don't forget the brackets.

e $(NH_4)_2SO_4$

Comment NH_4 combining power 1, SO_4 combining power 2. Don't forget the brackets.

Chemical equations (page 22)

Q1 a $C + O_2 \rightarrow CO_2$

Comment This doesn't need balancing!

b $4Fe + 3O_2 \rightarrow 2Fe_2O_3$

Comment Remember that balancing numbers must always go in front of symbols and formulae.

c $2Fe_2O_3 + 3C \rightarrow 4Fe + 3CO_2$

Comment One maths trick to use here is to realise that the number of oxygen atoms on the right-hand side must be even. Putting a '2' in front of Fe_2O_3 makes the oxygen on the left-hand side even too.

d $CaCO_3 + 2HCl \rightarrow CaCl_2 + CO_2 + H_2O$

Comment Note that the carbonate radical does not appear on both sides of the equation.

Q2 a $Ca^{2+} + CO_3^{2-} \rightarrow CaCO_3$

b $Fe^{2+} + 2OH^- \rightarrow Fe(OH)_2$

c $Ag^+ + Br^- \rightarrow AgBr$

Comment The symbols and charges must balance on each side of the equation. State symbols could be used,

e.g. $Fe^{2+}(aq) + 2OH^-(aq) \rightarrow Fe(OH)_2(s)$
$Ag^+(aq) + Br^-(aq) \rightarrow AgBr(s)$.

Q3 a $Al^{3+} + 3e^- \rightarrow Al$

b $Na \rightarrow Na^+ + e^-$

c $2O^{2-} \rightarrow O_2 + 4e^-$

d $2Br^- \rightarrow Br_2 + 2e^-$

Comment At the cathode positive ions gain electrons. At the anode negative ions lose electrons. Remember that symbols and charges must balance.

Q1 a 2 moles

Comment Moles = mass/RAM = 56/28 = 2

b 0.1 mole

Comment Moles = mass/RAM = 3.1/31 = 0.1

c 0.25 mole

Comment Moles = mass/RMM = 11/44 = 0.24

d 0.5 mole

Comment Moles = mass/RFM = 50/100 = 0.5
Note: Calcium carbonate is an ionic compound so the correct term is relative formula mass.

Q2 a 48 g

Comment Mass = moles × RAM = 2 × 24 = 48 g

b 4 g

Comment Mass = moles × RMM = 2 × 2 = 4 g

c 9.8 g

Comment Mass = moles × RMM = 0.1 × 98 = 9.8 g

Q3 $TiCl_4$

Comment	Ti	Cl
mass/RAM	25/48	75/35.5
moles	0.52	2.1
ratio	0.52/0.52 = 1	2.1/0.52 = 4.04
formula is $TiCl_4$		

Q4 a NaBr

Comment 0.1 mol Na reacts with 0.1 mol Br, i.e. ratio 1:1.

b CO_2

Comment 0.05 mol C reacts with 1.6/16 = 0.10 mol O, i.e. ratio 1:2.

c FeCl

Comment 0.2 mol Fe reacts with 7.1/35.5 = 0.2 mol Cl, i.e. ratio 1:1.

2 Equations and reacting masses (page 29)

Q1 4 g

Comment 2Na = 2 moles = 46 g. 2NaOH = 2 moles = 80 g. The scaling factor is ÷ 20.

Q2 a 560 tonnes

Comment Fe_2O_3 = 1 mole → 160 tonnes. 2Fe = 2 moles → 112 tonnes. The scaling factor is × 5.

b 144 litres at room temperature and pressure

Comment Fe_2O_3 = 1 mole → 160 g. $3CO_2$ = 3 × 24 = 72 litres. The scaling factor is × 2.

Q3 2.33 g

Comment $BaCl_2$ = 1 mole = 1000 cm³ (1 M). $BaSO_4$ = 1 mole = 233 g.
First scale by ÷ 5. 1000 cm³ (0.2 M) and 46.6 g.
Second scale by ÷ 20. 50 cm³ (0.2 M) and 2.33 g.

UNIT 4: THE PERIODIC TABLE AND ITS DEVELOPMENT
1 Organising the elements (pages 33–34)

Q1 a Dalton proposed atoms arranged in order of relative atomic mass.

Comment Dalton was still working on the assumption that atoms were small indivisible particles.

b Dobereiner arranged elements in groups of three (triads) based on similar properties.

Comment Only a few elements were known, so his pattern did not fit for all the elements discovered.

c Newlands proposed 'law of octaves', i.e. every eighth element had similar properties.

Comment Close to modern theory, but did not work for all known elements.

d Mendeleev accepted some elements had not been discovered, so arranged table to allow for this, i.e. left gaps which predicted the properties of elements still to be discovered.

Comment Still discrepancies because table still based on increasing atomic mass.

Q2 Modern table based on increasing atomic number (number of protons), not on 'atomic weight'.

Comment Atomic number allows correct link between position and properties.

Q3 a b

Comment Group 4 is the fourth major column from the left.

b a

Comment This is the second row.

c d

Comment The noble gas family is group 0 or 8.

d c

Comment Transition elements are in the middle block.

e b

Comment Metalloids are found near the 'staircase' on the right side of the periodic table, which separates metals from non-metals.

f d and f

Comment These are on the right of the 'staircase'. If you included b you would not be penalised.

g d

Comment Gases are non-metals and so have to be on the right side. f is a possibility but in groups 5, 6 and 7 elements near the bottom of the group are solids.

Q4 They contain the same number of electrons in the outer electron shell.

Comment Remember that how an atom reacts depends on its outermost electrons.

Q5 a B. Its pH is less than 7.

Comment Remember that the acidic oxide will also react with an alkali.

b A and B. Both react with an acid.

Comment 'A' has a pH of 7 because it doesn't dissolve in water.

c (i) Neutralisation

Comment Copper oxide is a base. The reaction of a base with an acid is neutralisation.

c (ii) Copper oxide + sulphuric acid → copper sulphate + water

Comment Remember that acid + base → salt + water.

c (iii) $CuO(s) + H_2SO_4(aq) \rightarrow CuSO_4(aq) + H_2O(l)$

Comment No extra balancing is required here.

c (iv) A.

Comment Copper(II) oxide is insoluble in water and so the mixture will have a pH of 7.

2 The metals (page 38)

Q1 a Caesium.

Comment Remember that the reactivity of metals increases down a group.

b To prevent the metal reacting with air and water.

Comment These are highly reactive metals. They oxidise rapidly without heat being needed.

c Caesium.

Comment The melting point gives a measure of hardness. Melting point decreases down the group.

d On cutting, the metal is exposed to the air and rapidly oxidises.

Comment Tarnishing is another word for oxidation.

e When added to water they react to produce an alkali.

Comment The metal hydroxides formed in the reactions are alkalis.

f Sodium is less dense than water.

Comment Density increases down the group. The more reactive metals would not float but their reaction is so violent that the metal usually flies out of the water!

g (i) rubidium + oxygen → rubidium oxide
$4Rb(s) + O_2(g) \rightarrow 2Rb_2O(s)$

Comment Rubidium behaves in the same way as sodium but more violently.

g (ii) caesium + water → caesium hydroxide + hydrogen
$2Cs(s) + 2H_2O(l) \rightarrow 2CsOH(aq) + H_2(g)$

Comment The reaction of the group 1 metals with water produces the metal hydroxide (an alkali) and hydrogen.

g (iii) potassium + chlorine → potassium chloride
$$2K(s) + Cl_2(g) \rightarrow 2KCl(s)$$

Comment Potassium chloride is a salt with an appearance very similar to sodium chloride, common salt.

Q2 a They are harder, have higher densities, higher melting points and are sonorous (any two).

Comment If you couldn't answer this look back at the summary on page 32.

b A catalyst is a substance that changes the speed of a chemical reaction without being changed itself.

Comment Catalysts and their effects on rates of reaction are covered in Unit 9.

c The alkali metals have only one electron in the outer electron shell. Transition metals have more than one electron in the outer electron shell.

Comment Reactivity is principally related to the number of electrons in the outer electron shell. Metals lower down a group are also more reactive than those higher up, but this is of secondary importance.

Q3 a A – sodium, B – copper, C – calcium.

Comment The sodium and calcium can be identified from the flame test information. Only one of the compounds contains a transition metal (forms a coloured compound).

b The hydroxides of the group 1 metals are soluble in water and would not form a precipitate.

Comment Calcium is in group 2. Calcium hydroxide is only sparingly soluble in water and so a precipitate forms.

c $Cu^{2+}(aq) + 2OH^-(aq) \rightarrow Cu(OH)_2(s)$

Comment The important part of the compound is the copper ion. The non-metal ion or radical does not play a part in the reaction - it is a spectator ion.

3 The non-metals (page 41)

Q1 a Fluorine

Comment Unlike groups of metals, reactivity decreases down the group.

b Bromine

Comment Bromine is the only liquid non-metal.

c Iodine

Comment Astatine would be expected to be a solid but it is radioactive with a very short half-life so it is difficult to confirm this prediction.

d They only need to gain one electron in order to have a full outer electron shell. Other non-metals need to gain more than one electron.

Comment Remember that reactivity depends on the number of electrons in the outer electron shell.

e (i) sodium + chlorine → sodium chloride
$$2Na(s) + Cl_2(g) \rightarrow 2NaCl(s)$$

e (ii) magnesium + bromine → magnesium bromide
$$Mg(s) + Br_2(l) \rightarrow MgBr_2(s)$$

Comment The halogen elements react with all metals. They form salts, called fluorides, chlorides, bromides and iodides.

e (iii) hydrogen + fluorine → hydrogen fluoride
$$H_2(g) + F_2(g) \rightarrow 2HF(g)$$

Comment Hydrogen fluoride will have very similar properties to the more familiar hydrogen chloride. Its solution in water, hydrofluoric acid, is highly corrosive.

Q2 a (i) Very pale yellow. (ii) Brown. (iii) Brown. (iv) Colourless.

Comment Bromine is more soluble in water than iodine but it is very difficult to distinguish between dilute solutions of the two. Sometimes a solvent like cyclohexane is added. The bromine is brown in the cyclohexane, the iodine is violet.

b On mixing the pale yellow solution with the colourless solution, a brown solution is formed.

Comment Observations are what you see, smell or hear. You don't see bromine; you see a brown solution.

c X ✓ ✓
X X ✓
X X X

Comment The more reactive halogen will displace (take the place of) the less reactive halogen. Chlorine will displace bromine from sodium bromide because it is more reactive. Iodine cannot replace chlorine or bromine as it is less reactive than both of them.

d Bromine + sodium iodide → iodine + sodium bromide
$Br_2(aq) + 2NaI(aq) \rightarrow I_2(aq) + 2NaBr(aq)$

Comment Bromine is more reactive than iodine and so will displace it from the solution. In this reaction it would be difficult to see a change as both the bromine and iodine solutions are brown. Using cyclohexane would confirm that a reaction had taken place.

Q3 Noble gases have full outer electron shells and so do not need to gain or lose electrons in a reaction.

Comment Remember that metals want to lose electrons and form positive ions, whereas non-metals often try to gain electrons and form negative ions. Details of ionic bonding are given in Unit 1.

UNIT 5: CHEMICALS FROM OIL
I Processing crude oil (pages 45–46)

Q1 a Small sea creatures died, their bodies settled in the mud at the bottom of the oceans and decayed. They were compressed over a period of millions of years and slowly changed into crude oil.

Comment Remember the process involves compression and takes place over millions of years. Do not confuse crude oil with coal, which is formed from plant material.

b It takes millions of years to form. Once supplies have been used up they cannot be replaced.

Comment A common mistake is to say 'it cannot be used again'. No fuel can be used again but some, such as trees (wood), can be regrown quite quickly. Wood is therefore renewable.

Q2 a Fractional distillation.

Comment There is often a mark for 'fractional' and a mark for 'distillation'.

b The boiling point of the fractions decreases.

Comment Remember the column is hotter at the bottom than at the top.

c Components that have boiling points just above the temperature of X will condense to a liquid. Components which have boiling points below the temperature of X will remain as vapour and continue up the column.

Comment If a vapour is cooled below its boiling point it will condense.

d The component would be not very runny (it would be viscous), very dark yellow/orange in colour, very difficult to light and very smoky when burning.

Comment Again the clues are in the table. A fuel needs to ignite easily and be 'clean'.

e It would not ignite easily. It would produce a lot of soot when burning.

Comment In a question like this, the clues to the answer will be in the table. Always give as full an answer as possible. Four points can be scored using the last three columns of the table.

Q3 a A compound containing carbon and hydrogen atoms only.

Comment Don't miss out the word 'only'. A lot of compounds contain carbon and hydrogen but are not hydrocarbons (e.g. glucose, $C_6H_{12}O_6$).

b High temperature, catalyst.

Comment 'Catalytic crackers' are used at oil refineries.

c C_8H_{18}.

Comment The equation must balance so the number of carbon atoms must be 10 – 2, the number of hydrogen atoms 22 – 4.

Q4 a Larger straight-chain molecules are broken down into smaller molecules that are re-joined to form branched-chain molecules.

Comment You need to recognise the difference in the changes to molecules during reforming as compared to cracking.

b High-grade petrol is mainly branched-chain molecules because they catch fire at the correct temperature in the combustion chamber.

Comment It is important to know that straight-chain molecules catch fire more readily than branched-chain molecules.

2 How are hydrocarbons used? (page 50)

Q1 a petrol + oxygen → carbon dioxide + water

Comment All hydrocarbons produce carbon dioxide and water when burnt in a plentiful supply of air. It is much better to use oxygen rather than air in the equation.

b Shortage of oxygen.

Comment Remember this is incomplete combustion.

c The carbon monoxide combines with the haemoglobin in the blood, preventing oxygen from doing so. Supply of oxygen to the body is reduced. Specifically this can quickly cause the death of brain cells.

Comment A much more detailed answer is required than 'it causes suffocation'.

Q2 a (i)

hexane

(ii)

hexene

Comment Remember 'hex' means 6. The ending 'ane' means only single bonds whereas 'ene' means there is a carbon–carbon double bond.

b Add bromine water. It will be decolourised by hexene but not by hexane.

Comment This is the standard test for all alkenes. You should give the test reagent and what you would observe.

Q3 a

Comment 'Prop' means 3 carbon atoms.

b

Comment If you had problems here look back at how ethene polymerises. Then replace one H atom by a CH_3 group.

c Poly(propene).

Comment Just put 'poly' in front of the name of the monomer.

d Propane is saturated and doesn't have a carbon–carbon double bond to undergo addition reactions.

Comment The carbon–carbon double bond is the reactive part of the molecule.

Unit 6: The changing earth
1 Geological change (page 56)

Q1 a Earthquakes (or volcanoes).

Comment Remember that earthquakes occur when two plates rub together.

b As the two plates move apart a weakness forms in the crust. Magma from the mantle is forced up, cools and forms igneous rock.

Comment Igneous rocks are formed when the lava from a volcano cools. Volcanoes are not always formed – sometimes the magma doesn't break through the crust.

c High temperature and high pressure.

Comment As the oceanic plate is forced into the mantle the rocks are squashed and heated.

Q2 a Convection currents in the liquid mantle.

Comment Energy from the core is transferred to the mantle, causing convection currents.

b If two continental plates collide mountains form. If a continental plate collides with an oceanic plate then an ocean trench forms.

Comment You need to distinguish between the two types of plate.

Q3 *Weathering* – water gets into cracks in the rocks and then freezes and expands. As the ice melts, fragments of rock break away.
Erosion – running water and strong winds carrying sand can wear rocks away. Acid rain dissolves limestone. *Transportation* – rain water carries particles into streams and rivers.

Comment It is important that you are clear about these three processes. If not, look back at the diagram on page 54. The differences between weathering and erosion are slight and so you shouldn't worry if you had trouble separating them. This is a very common examination question.

Q4 a Originally, all the continents were joined together to make one super-continent (named Pangaea). This broke up into the separate continents and they drifted apart to their present positions.

Comment The basis of the theory is that a large land mass split up into smaller pieces which moved apart.

b Shapes of continents seem to fit together like jigsaw pieces, e.g. Africa and South America. Similar fossils found on several continents. Similar rocks found in mountain ranges of several different continents.

Comment Remembering these three pieces of evidence is vital to any answer on tectonic plates/continental drift.

c The Earth was hot when it was formed. As it cooled, the crust formed which shrank as cooling continued, so forming the mountain ranges and other features of the Earth's surface, i.e. a wrinkling effect.

Comment If 'hot → cold → contraction → wrinkling' is remembered, you will be able to present the original theory correctly.

2 Changes to the atmosphere (page 62)

Q1 a Photosynthesis.

> **Comment** You need to remember that plants absorb CO_2 and give out O_2.

   a Respiration and combustion.

> **Comment** Until the last 200 years, combustion played a small part. It is now a bigger part of the problem and the build-up of CO_2 is contributing to the greenhouse effect and global warming.

Q2 The greenhouse effect describes how some of the gases in the atmosphere prevent heat escaping from the Earth. Global warming is an increase in the Earth's temperature that may well be caused by an increased greenhouse effect.

> **Comment** Remember that it is the *increased* greenhouse effect that people are concerned about. A greenhouse effect is essential to keep the life on Earth sustainable – without it there would be another ice age.

Q3 a Burning fossil fuels that contain both sulphur and nitrogen. The oxides of sulphur and nitrogen react with water to form acids, e.g. sulphuric acid.

> **Comment** The key point is the presence of sulphur and nitrogen $\rightarrow SO_2$ (and NO_2) and so to H_2SO_4.

   b Effect of sulphuric acid on buildings made of limestone/marble or metal.
Effect on plants, leading to effect on animals.
Leaching into rivers and lakes of aluminium which poisons fish.

> **Comment** There are many effects of acid rain and you need to focus on the key facts relating to the environment and hence animals/fish/plants.

Q4 An increase in the rate of skin cancer.

> **Comment** The ozone layer prevents too much UV light from the Sun reaching the Earth's surface. Ozone depletion by the effect of CFCs means more UV rays reaching the surface and increasing skin cancers.

3 Changes to rivers and seas (page 66)

Q1 Evaporation (liquid to gas/vapour) and condensation (gas/vapour to liquid).

> **Comment** 78% of the Earth's surface is covered by water (the seas and oceans).
> Heat from the Sun evaporates the water to form clouds (water vapour) which then rise (so cooling) and the water vapour condenses to form raindrops.

Q2 a Any 2 from the following:
Increased demand for food as population increases.
Need for better quality crops.
Need for larger amount of crops.
Need for faster production of crops.
Economically better if more crops can be grown quicker.

> **Comment** The link between the need for more food as the world's population increases is important. However, food production is an 'industry' and the economics of it is a very important factor.

   b When it rains the fertilisers dissolve and are washed through the ground into streams and rivers. They cause algae to grow on the surface which eventually cut off the light reaching plants in the water. These plants die and bacteria that consume them use up the oxygen in the water. Fish with no oxygen to breathe then die.

> **Comment** The process of eutrophication is best remembered as: fertiliser $\rightarrow$ algae $\rightarrow$ reduced light $\rightarrow$ plants die $\rightarrow$ bacteria take oxygen $\rightarrow$ fish die. A common error is ignore the algae and use 'increased plant growth' which absorb the oxygen. Plants give out oxygen (photosynthesis).

Q3 As rain water falls through the atmosphere it dissolves carbon dioxide to form a weak acid (carbonic acid). When this weak acid reaches the sea it reacts with the calcium and magnesium ions to form soluble calcium and magnesium hydrogencarbonates as well as the insoluble calcium carbonate (which sinks to the floor of the sea as sediment).

Comment The formulae of the chemicals involved are relevant to a full answer, i.e. carbonic acid H_2CO_3, calcium hydrogencarbonate $Ca(HCO_3)_2$, magnesium hydrogencarbonate $Mg(HCO_3)_2$, calcium carbonate $CaCO_3$.

UNIT 7: ACIDS, BASES, ALKALIS AND SALTS

I What are acids, bases and alkalis? (page 70)

Q1 a A substance that changes colour to show if a solution is acidic, neutral or alkaline (basic).

Comment Litmus as red, purple or blue is linked to acidic; neutral and alkaline need to be remembered as conditions shown by an indicator.

b The numbers 1 to 14 linked to the strengths of acids and alkalis (bases).

Comment pH 1 to 6 is strongly acidic to weakly acidic, pH 7 is neutral and pH 8 to 14 is weakly alkaline to strongly alkaline.

c Each colour from Universal Indicator has a pH number.

Comment Remember pH 1-2 is maroon/red, pH 7 is yellow-green and pH 13-14 is blue/purple.

Q2 a An acid that totally dissociates into ions, so releasing all its available H^+ ions.

Comment This is 'strong' as opposed to 'weak' (partial dissociation).

b $H_3PO_4(aq) \rightarrow 3H^+(aq) + PO_4^{3-}(aq)$

Comment For a strong acid you need to use the arrow symbol, $\rightarrow$. Phosphoric acid is tribasic, so producing $3 \times H^+$.

c pH = 1 to 2

Comment Strong acids are in this range on the pH scale, and maroon/red as UI colours.

Q3 $LiOH(aq) \rightarrow Li^+(aq) + OH^-(aq)$

Comment Lithium is in group 1, the same as sodium and potassium, so is a strong alkali. This needs the arrow symbol for complete dissociation to ions.

Q4 a Only partially dissociates into ions.

Comment As opposed to 'strong' which is complete dissociation to ions.

b $HCOOH(aq) \rightleftharpoons HCOO^-(aq) + H^+(aq)$

Comment Methanoic acid is monobasic (one H^+) and, since it is weak, there is an equilibrium shown by the $\rightleftharpoons$ sign.

2 Making salts (page 74)

Q1 a $K_2SO_4(aq) + 2H_2O(l)$

Comment alkali + acid $\rightarrow$ soluble salt + water

b $MgCl_2(aq) + H_2O(l)$

Comment acid + base $\rightarrow$ soluble salt + water

c $Ba(NO_3)_2(aq) + CO_2(g) + H_2O(l)$

Comment acid + carbonate $\rightarrow$ soluble salt + carbon dioxide + water

d $ZnCl_2(aq) + H_2(g)$

Comment acid + metal $\rightarrow$ soluble salt + hydrogen

e $ZnCO_3(s) + 2KCl(aq)$

Comment soluble salt + soluble salt $\rightarrow$ insoluble salt + soluble salt
The issue is which of the two salts is insoluble. You need to remember that in this method it is usually sodium or potassium salts that are used as one of the reactants – sodium and potassium salts are almost always soluble.

Q2 Put some dilute sulphuric acid into a beaker and add copper(II) oxide until it is **in excess**. Filter the mixture through a filter paper in a funnel to remove the excess copper(II) oxide. The liquid collected in an evaporating dish is copper(II) sulphate solution.

The evaporating dish is put on a gauze on a tripod and heated with a Bunsen burner to evaporate some of the water. The hot solution is poured into the dish to cool, and crystals of the salt are formed. The dish is left until all the water evaporates and only the crystals are left.

Comment The information in the question about the reagents and the salt show this is the preparation of a *soluble* salt, i.e. crystals.
acid + base → soluble salt + water

Q3 a $H_2SO_4(aq) + Zn(s) \rightarrow ZnSO_4(aq) + H_2(g)$

Comment Zinc is a metal, so the method is:
    acid + metal → soluble salt + hydrogen
Sulphuric acid forms sulphate.

b $HCl(aq) + KOH(aq) \rightarrow KCl(aq) + H_2O(l)$

Comment To make a chloride requires hydrochloric acid, and the KOH being a solution means it is an alkali, not just a base.
The method is:
    acid + alkali → soluble salt + water

c $2HNO_3(aq) + CuCO_3(s) \rightarrow Cu(NO_3)_2(aq) + CO_2 9g) + H_2O(l)$

Comment Nitrates are made from nitric acid, and the carbonate shows which of the 5 methods to use.
    acid + carbonate →soluble salt + carbon dioxide + water

d $MgCl_2(aq) + 2KCO_3(aq) \rightarrow MgCO_3(s) + 2KCl(aq)$

Comment The reactants are two soluble salts, and so is the product potassium chloride. So magnesium carbonate must be an insoluble salt for it to be possible to separate it, as a precipitate.
The method is:
    soluble salt + soluble salt → insoluble salt + soluble salt

e $2HCl(aq) + ZnO(s) \rightarrow ZnCl_2(aq) + H_2O(l)$

Comment The zinc oxide is a solid, and oxides are bases. The method uses hydrochloric acid to make the chloride, so the general method is:
    acid + base → soluble salt + water

3 Sodium chloride and the chlor-alkali industry (page 78)

Q1 Sodium chloride is soluble in water, coal is insoluble.

Comment A fundamental fact about NaCl; the solution is called brine.

Q2 a Cathode: $2H^+(aq) + 2e^- \rightarrow H_2(g)$
Anode: $2Cl^-(aq) \rightarrow Cl_2(g) + 2e^-$

Comment These two elements are diatomic gaseous molecules.

b Removal of H^+ and Cl^- from the solution leaves Na^+ and OH^-, i.e. NaOH(aq).

Comment It is important to remember there are *four* ions in sodium chloride solution.

Q3 'Chlor' comes from chlorine gas, and 'alkali' from sodium hydroxide.

Comment Because only two products are mentioned in the term, do not forget there are three products of the process, i.e. hydrogen as well.

Q4 The chlorine and sodium hydroxide would react together to make NaOCl.

Comment The tests and uses need to be learned thoroughly.

Q5 a Chlorine bleaches damp litmus paper. It is used to kill bacteria in drinking water.

b Hydrogen 'pops' with a lighted splint. It is used to make margarine.

Comment The fact that they react is the basic idea; quoting the product of the reaction is the fuller answer.

UNIT 8: RESOURCES FROM THE EARTH

Extraction of metals (page 85)

Q1 a Iron oxide + carbon → iron + carbon dioxide

Comment In the blast furnace much of the reduction is done by carbon monoxide.

b Reduced. Reduction is the loss of oxygen. The iron oxide has lost oxygen, forming iron.

Comment Reduction and oxidation always occur together. In this reaction the carbon is oxidised.

c The limestone reacts with impurities, forming a slag that floats to the top and is removed from the furnace.

Comment Of the three raw materials in the blast furnace (coke, iron ore, limestone) this is the easiest one to forget.

Q2 a This is the breakdown (decomposition) of a compound using electricity.

Comment If you are still puzzled by electrolysis look back at page 81.

b This is a substance which when molten or dissolved in water allows an electric current to pass through it.

Comment Electrolytes must contain ions and the ions must be free to move before a current will flow.

c This is the substance which makes the electrical contact between the battery and the electrolyte.

Comment In a circuit there will always be two electrodes.

d This is the electrode connected to the positive terminal of the battery.

Comment Ions that travel to the anode are called anions (negatively charged ions).

e This is the electrode connected to the negative terminal of the battery.

Comment Ions that travel to the cathode are called cations (positively charged ions).

Q3 a The ions must be free to move. In a solid the ions are held in a giant lattice structure.

Comment Remember that the ions in a solid can be made free to move by either melting the solid or dissolving it in water. Aluminium oxide does not dissolve in water.

b Cathode.

Comment Aluminium ions are positively charged and so will be attracted to the negative electrode.

c Aluminium ions gain electrons and form aluminium atoms.

$$Al^{3+} + 3e^- \rightarrow Al$$

Comment The ionic equation must balance in terms of symbols and charges.

d The oxygen that is produced at the anode oxidises the hot carbon electrodes, forming carbon dioxide.

Comment This is one of the drawbacks of the method and also adds to the expense of producing aluminium.

Q4 a Al_2O_3 is an ionic compound and conducts electricity. TiO_2 is a covalent compound, it does not conduct electricity, so electrolysis cannot be used to extract it.

Comment The fact that TiO_2 is a covalent compound is unusual and the reason for the method of extraction used.

b TiO_2 is converted to $TiCl_4$ by heating it with carbon and passing chlorine over it at about 900 °C:

$$TiO_2 + C + 2Cl_2 \rightarrow TiCl_4 + CO_2$$

The $TiCl_4$ is reacted with sodium (or magnesium) to produce the titanium:

$$TiCl_4 + 4Na \rightarrow Ti + 4NaCl$$

Comment This is the extraction process stripped down to the basics. The question asks for two equations but *not* the state symbols, so these have been omitted. The chemical principles are not asked for, so the issue of sodium (or magnesium) being more reactive has not been included. Sodium was chosen for the equation of the second reaction because NaCl is easier to remember than $MgCl_2$.

c *Either:* In the first stage (TiO_2 to $TiCl_4$) the titanium is losing oxygen – this is reduction.

Or: In the second stage the Ti in $TiCl_4$ is gaining four electrons to become a titanium atom – this is reduction.

Comment There are two reduction processes involved in the extraction of titanium. The question is not specific, so you can choose stage 1 or 2 of the process for your answer.

2 The limestone industry (page 88)

Q1 Limestone can be converted into quicklime, and quicklime into slaked lime. All three materials have a wide variety of uses.

Comment This is the basis of the huge amounts quarried. There is no need to give a specific use in this answer.

Q2 a $CaCO_3(s) \rightarrow CaO(s) + CO_2(g)$

b $CaO(s) + H_2O(l) \rightarrow Ca(OH)_2(s)$

Comment Both equations are pivotal to the topic and need to be thoroughly learned. State symbols are essential.

Q3 a Pass the gas though limewater. If the limewater turns cloudy/milky, the gas is carbon dioxide.

b $Ca(OH)_2(aq) + CO_2(aq) \rightarrow CaCO_3(s) + H_2O(l)$

Comment The limewater test for CO_2 is a key chemical test, and the cause of the cloudy/milky colour is the formation of insoluble calcium carbonate (limestone) as a *precipitate*, i.e. a solid formed in a solution.

Q4 Limestone is used to neutralise the acidic gases, e.g. sulphur dioxide produced by burning fossil fuels. The equation is:

$$CaCO_3 + H_2SO_4 \rightarrow CaSO_3 + H_2O + CO_2$$

Comment This would be a 2 marks question, giving the 'clue' that the equation is also needed. Limestone to neutralise acidity is the key for the first mark, with the second mark for the chemical equation. Note that $H_2O + SO_2 \rightarrow H_2SO_3$, 'sulphurous acid' is first formed. It then oxidises in the air to sulphuric acid.

UNIT 9: CHEMICAL REACTIONS
Chemical change (page 92)

Q1 Not all collisions provide enough energy for the reaction to take place.

Comment Energy is needed to break chemical bonds so that the atoms, molecules or ions can rearrange and form new bonds. Remember that collisions that do have sufficient energy are referred to as **effective collisions**.

Q2 Reaction A.

Comment Reaction A has a lower activation energy than reaction B. This means that there will be more effective collisions and so the rate of reaction will be higher. If you are still not clear about this idea of an 'energy barrier', look again at the explanation of activation energy in the **collision theory** section.

Q3 a Carbon dioxide

Comment Remember that marble has the chemical name calcium carbonate. The carbon dioxide is released from the carbonate ion.

b (i) 20 cm^3; (ii) 16 cm^3; (iii) 13 cm^3; (iv) 0 cm^3.

Comment 20 − 0 = 20; 36 − 20 = 16; 49 − 36 = 13; 70 − 70 = 0. Don't forget the units of volume.

c The volume of gas produced in each 10 second interval decreases as the reaction proceeds. This means the rate of production of gas decreases.

Comment The rate of reaction is measured in terms of the volume of gas produced in a certain amount of time. If you wanted to calculate rates in these time intervals you would need to divide the volume of gas produced by the time taken. So between 0 and 10 seconds 20 cm^3 of gas was collected giving a rate of 20/10 = 2 cm^3/s. Between 20 and 30 seconds the rate was 1.3 cm^3/s.

d As the reaction proceeds there are fewer particles of hydrochloric acid and calcium carbonate to collide with each other. Therefore there will be fewer collisions and hence fewer effective collisions.

Comment Don't forget to mention the idea of 'effective collisions' (see page 89). This is a key idea in this chapter. If you want to impress the examiner use the correct names for the particles – e.g. in this reaction collisions occur between hydrogen ions (H$^+$ ions) and carbonate ions (CO$_3^{2-}$ ions).

e Measuring the change in mass as the reaction proceeds.

Comment The carbon dioxide gas will escape, causing a decrease in mass of the reaction container. The equipment you would need is shown on page 91.

2 Controlling the rate of reaction (page 96)

Q1 As the temperature increases, the kinetic energy of the reacting particles also increases. The particles will therefore be moving faster and will collide more frequently. In addition, there will be more energy transferred in the collisions and so more are likely to be effective and lead to a reaction.

Comment Don't forget to mention the energy of the collision. Many students only mention the increased number of collisions.

Q2 a (i) Experiment 1; (ii) the reaction finishes more quickly because the curve levels out soonest.

Comment A better answer would mention the gradient of the curve – e.g. the gradient of the curve at the beginning of the reaction is the steepest.

b (i) Experiment 3; (ii) the largest chips have the smallest surface area and so the lowest rate of reaction.

Comment The curve for experiment 3 has the lowest gradient at the beginning of the reaction. If you got this wrong check the section on **surface area** again.

c (i) 7.5 minutes (approximately); (ii) the reaction finished because the marble was used up.

Comment Try to read off the graph as accurately as you can. In an examination you will be allowed a small margin of error. In this example 7.3 to 7.7 minutes would be acceptable. The question says that the hydrochloric acid was 'an excess'. This means that there was more than would be needed. Therefore the reaction must have finished because the marble was used up. Always look for the phrase 'an excess' or 'in excess'.

d The same mass of marble was used in each experiment.

Comment As the acid is in excess the amount of marble will determine how much carbon dioxide is produced.

e The curve would be steeper (have a higher gradient) at the beginning of the reaction but would reach the same plateau height.

Comment Increasing the temperature will increase the rate of the reaction but will not change the amount of carbon dioxide produced. If you are still in doubt about this read the section on **temperature** again.

Q3 a A catalyst is a substance that alters the rate of a chemical reaction but does not change itself.

Comment Remember that whilst most catalysts speed up reactions some slow them down.

b A catalyst provides another route for the reaction with a different activation energy.

Comment Think of activation energy as an energy barrier that prevents reactants changing into products.

3 Making use of enzymes (page 99)

Q1 A biological catalyst.

Comment A really good answer would include the fact that they are protein molecules.

Q2 a Yeast.

b The brewing and baking industries.

Comment Remember that the ethanol is the more important product in the brewing industry and that the carbon dioxide is more important in the baking industry.

c At higher temperatures the enzymes present in the yeast are denatured and can no longer act as catalysts.

Comment A common mistake is to say that the 'enzymes are killed' at higher temperatures. Enzymes are not alive in the first place!

d glucose $\rightarrow$ ethanol + carbon dioxide

e $C_6H_{12}O_6 \rightarrow 2C_2H_5OH + 2CO_2$

Comment Remember when balancing an equation that the balancing numbers can only be placed in front of the formulae (see Unit 2).

Q3 a An active site is the part of an enzyme molecule in which reactant molecules are trapped.

Comment You can think of it as a hole or cavity.

b The arrangement and shape of the active site in an enzyme will only 'fit' one specific type of molecule.

Comment This is sometimes referred to as a 'lock and key' model – only one key fits the lock.

Q4 a Enzymes work at lower temperatures and pressures than other catalysts. This means that they reduce the need for expensive equipment and reduce energy costs. They are also biodegradable, so do not damage the environment.

Disadvantages are that pure enzymes can be expensive to produce and can be wasteful if 'lost' at the end of the process.

Comment These advantages/disadvantages are key ideas in the use of enzymes by industry.

b In batch processing, it is a 'one-off' process and it has to be stopped, then started up again. The enzymes are often 'lost' at the end of the process.

Continuous processing means the product is continually being made, which is what industry prefers. Also, the enzymes are not lost in the process.

Comment Sometimes continuous processing cannot be used, e.g. in washing machines using biological detergents in the home.

c 'Stabilising' means the enzymes can be kept working for a longer time. 'Immobilising' means trapping the enzyme on an inert solid support, e.g. beads, so it is not lost in the process.

Comment For 'stabilising' you need to just explain 'longevity' but for 'immobilising' you need to explain how it is done as well as the idea of not 'losing' the enzyme.

UNIT 10: ENERGY AND EQUILIBRIA
1 Energy changes (page 104)

Q1 a Energy = $40 \times 4.2 \times 32 = 5376$ J.

b Energy = $5376/0.2 = 26\,880$ J/g.

Comment Use the formula energy = mass $\times$ 4.2 $\times$ temperature change.

Q2 a The reaction is exothermic.

b More energy is released when bonds are formed than is used to break the bonds in the first place.

Comment In an energy level diagram, if the products are lower in energy than the reactants the reaction change is exothermic. Remember that the overall energy change = energy needed to break bonds – energy released on forming bonds.

Q3 More energy is released when the H—Cl bonds are made than is needed to break the H—H and Cl—Cl bonds. The overall energy change is therefore exothermic.

Comment Again this refers to the balance between bond breaking and bond forming. Always refer to the specific bonds involved.

Q4 a Total bonds on left:

$4 \times$ C–H	4×413
$2 \times$ O=O	2×498
Total	$+2648$ kJ mol^{-1}

Total bonds on right:

$2 \times$ C=O	2×745	$= 1490$
$4 \times$ O–H	4×464	
Total	-3346 kJ mol^{-1}	

Overall: -3346
        $+2648$
        -698

Answer: $\Delta H = -698$ kJ mol^{-1}

Comment The bonds on the left of the equation are broken, so a + sign; those on the right are made, so a – sign.

b The – sign shows the reaction is exothermic.

Comment In a question of this type, even if you make an error in the sign you will gain the mark for correctly liking it to exothermic or endothermic.

2 Chemical equilibria (page 108)

Q1 A reaction is in equilibrium when the number of reactant and product molecules do not change.

Comment You might remember that at equilibrium the rate of the forward reaction equals the rate of the backward reaction.

Q2 a The rate changes (usually increases).

Comment Catalysts are usually used to increase reaction rate.

b No effect.

Comment A catalyst does not change the position of equilibrium.

Q3 The higher temperature is used to increase the rate of the reaction.

Comment The choice of temperature in industrial processes often balances how much can be formed (depends on the equilibrium position) and how fast it can be formed (depends on the rate of the reaction).

Q4 The reaction:

$$SO_3(g) + H_2O(l) \rightarrow H_2SO_4(l)$$

is very exothermic. The heat makes the acid vaporise into a dangerous 'acid mist'.

Comment To make sulphuric acid by way of 'oleum' seems unnecessary, until you recognise the exothermic nature of the reaction above.

UNIT 11: ORGANIC CHEMISTRY
1 Hydrocarbons (page 112)

Q1 a Members of the same family which differ by one carbon atom each time, i.e. $-CH_2-$ is added.

b Molecules with the same number and type of atoms but arranged in different ways.

Comment Questions on alkanes and alkenes will almost always ask you for one of these terms – sometimes both of them.

Q2 a Two isomers of hexane:

and

b Two isomers of butene:

and

Comment It is always easiest to draw the long straight-chain isomer, then to take a $-CH_3$ off one end and put it somewhere else in the, now shorter, chain.
Don't forget to count the C's and H's to make sure they add up to the original formula.

Q3 The molecules have intermolecular forces between them. The longer the chain the greater these are, so the boiling points increase with length of chain.

Comment Sometimes, this idea is tested by giving you two or three isomers and asking you to say which would have the highest boiling point, when you should identify the molecule with the longest carbon chain.

2 Alcohols and carboxylic acids (page 119)

Q1 a Yeast contains an enzyme that converts sugar to ethanol. Enzymes work at a low optimum temperature. If the temperature rises above 30 °C, the enzyme is denatured and the reaction stops.

Comment This topic involves work on enzymes from Unit 9, and the basic facts about these biological catalysts is an integral part of the work on fermentation.

b Oxygen from the air would oxidise the ethanol to ethanoic acid ('vinegar'). This is 'spoilage'.

Comment As an oxidation process, changing alcohols to carboxylic acids, is a fundamental part of the chemistry syllabus.

Q2 Two isomers of butanol:

$$H-\overset{\overset{\displaystyle H}{|}}{\underset{\underset{\displaystyle H}{|}}{C}}-\overset{\overset{\displaystyle H}{|}}{\underset{\underset{\displaystyle H}{|}}{C}}-\overset{\overset{\displaystyle H}{|}}{\underset{\underset{\displaystyle H}{|}}{C}}-\overset{\overset{\displaystyle H}{|}}{\underset{\underset{\displaystyle H}{|}}{C}}-OH$$

and

$$H-\overset{\overset{\displaystyle H}{|}}{\underset{\underset{\displaystyle H}{|}}{C}}-\overset{\overset{\displaystyle H}{|}}{\underset{\underset{\displaystyle H}{|}}{C}}-\overset{\overset{\displaystyle OH}{|}}{\underset{\underset{\displaystyle H}{|}}{C}}-\overset{\overset{\displaystyle H}{|}}{\underset{\underset{\displaystyle H}{|}}{C}}-OH$$

Comment As with the isomers of hydrocarbons, the simplest way is the best in such questions. Start with the −OH group at the end of the longest straight carbon chain and then put it on another carbon atom in the chain.

Q3 The reaction between an alcohol and a carboxylic acid to form an ester.

Comment This is a basic reaction of alcohols and carboxylic acids. Esters are vital components of perfumes.

Q4 Dip in Universal Indicator paper – it will show a pH of 4 to 6.

Comment This is the easiest way to recognise that a solution is a weak acid. However, you need to recognise that these compounds are weak acids, so will react with carbonates (e.g. Na_2CO_3) or hydrogencarbonates (e.g. $NaHCO_3$) to give off CO_2 (turning limewater cloudy/milky).

UNIT 12: AQUEOUS CHEMISTRY
1 Hardness of water (page 123)

Q1 a Rainwater contains dissolved carbon dioxide, so making it weakly acidic:
$$H_2O(l) + CO_2(g) \rightarrow H_2CO_3(aq)$$

The carbonic acid reacts with limestone and dissolves it as calcium hydrogencarbonate solution:
$$H_2CO_3(aq) + CaCO_3(s) \rightarrow Ca(HCO_3)_2(aq)$$

As the solution goes into the caverns the calcium hydrogencarbonate gives off H_2O and CO_2, and the solid calcium carbonate is left to form the stalactites and stalagmites:
$$Ca(HCO_3)_2(aq) \rightarrow CaCO_3(s) + H_2O(l) + CO_2(g)$$

Comment This question shows the importance of knowing both the equation and the state symbols to explain the importance of:
$$(s) \rightarrow (aq) \text{ and } (aq) \rightarrow (s)$$

Q2 a Sample B

Comment Easy! It requires the least number of soap drops to give a lather.

b Calcium sulphate – this is permanent hardness since boiling has little effect on the hardness of the water.

c Calcium hydrogencarbonate – this is temporary hardness since boiling softens it.

Comment These issues are central to permanent vs. temporary hardness in the topic. In part c, magnesium hydrogencarbonate would be an equally acceptable answer.

d calcium + sodium → calcium + sodium
sulphate stearate stearate sulphate
(soap) (scum)

*Comment This is a word equation, but you do
need to identify the 'soap' and the 'scum'.*

Q3 a Distillation involves boiling the hard water and
collecting the pure water as it evaporates off.
The energy needed is expensive, so not used
on a large scale.

*Comment You need to link 'distillation' to heat
energy (liquid → vapour → liquid) to identify the
cost factor.*

b $CaSO_4(aq) + Na_2CO_3(aq) → CaCO_3(s) + Na_2SO_4(aq)$

*Comment This equation needs to be learnt, as
does the fact that 'washing soda' is sodium
carbonate, Na_2CO_3.*

c The Ca^{2+} and Mg^{2+} ions cause the hardness
and are 'trapped' on the resin, replaced by
Na^+ ions. The resin becomes full of Ca^{2+} and
Mg^{2+} – they are flushed out (the resin is
'regenerated') by pouring concentrated
sodium chloride solution through the resin.

*Comment The commonest questions are about
'modern' water-softening techniques.*

d Contains more Na^+ ions than hard water.
Sodium is linked to heart disease.

Soft water dissolves metal water pipes, so
poisonous metals (e.g. lead) can get into the
drinking water.

*Comment It is easy to overlook the
disadvantages of soft water when much of the
topic is about 'softening hard water', implying it
is preferable!*

2 Solubility - water as a solvent for gases and liquids (page 125)

Q1 a Gases dissolve better in cold water than hot
water. The bubbles are oxygen and carbon
dioxide coming out of the water.

b In the bottle the liquid is under pressure, so
the carbon dioxide stays dissolved in the
water (gases dissolve better under high
pressure). When the top is removed, the
pressure is released and, if left, the carbon
dioxide comes out of the water and the drink
goes 'flat'.

*Comment These two questions examine the basic
facts about dissolving gases in water, i.e. most
gas will be dissolved at low temperatures and
high pressures.*

Q2 a More of the solid can be dissolved in the
solution.

b If more solid is added it will not dissolve, it
will just sink to the bottom.

*Comment The concept of saturated/unsaturated
is central to the topic of dissolving solids in
water and solubility curves.*

Q3 a Between 35 and 45 g/100g water

b Between 53 and 60 °C.

*Comment Reading off the curves should be
straightforward. The scale of the graph makes
it hard to make accurate readings – the mark
scheme would allow between 35 – 45g for part
a and 53–60 °C for part b.*

Q3 c At 100 °C: 65g/100g water

At 60 °C: 50g/100g water

65 – 50 = 15 g (Between 13 and 18 g.)

*Comment The scale again is difficult to read
accurately at 100°C, so the mark scheme answer
would be between 12 and 18 g.*

Unit 13: Identifying Elements, Compounds and Ions
1 Techniques used in the laboratory (page 130)

Q1 'Corrosive' means it can damage the skin, so gloves should be worn when handling it. Because it is 'highly flammable' it gives off vapours (evaporates easily) so it should be used in a fume cupboard so that it does not catch fire.

Comment You cannot give the safety precautions needed without explaining the specific effects indicated by the hazard symbols.

Q2 Put a piece of damp blue litmus paper which will go first red (it is acidic), then white (it is a bleach).

Comment The tests for gases need to be learnt. The test for chlorine is the least well known by students!

Q3 To test for the cation, add sodium hydroxide solution and a white precipitate will be formed. If the precipitate dissolves when excess sodium hydroxide solution is added, Al^{3+} is present. If it does not dissolve in excess, then Mg^{2+} or Ca^{2+} is present. Perform a flame test on the solution – a brick red colour identifies Ca^{2+}; if not a red colour, it is Mg^{2+}.

Comment These three cations are commonly examined on the Higher Tier papers.

Q4 The colours show that the white solid is zinc carbonate and the gas is carbon dioxide.

Comment Zinc carbonate (white/yellow/white) and copper carbonate (green/black) are specifically identified by their distinctive colour changes on heating/cooling.

2 Modern instrumental methods (page 133)

Q1 Only very small samples need to be used because these methods are accurate, sensitive and very quick.

Comment These are the basic reasons why modern instruments are used.

Q2 Elements – flame photometry. Its advantage is that it is fast and very sensitive. A disadvantage is it cannot detect non-metal ions.

Compounds – chromatography techniques, e.g. liquid-liquid. Advantage of these techniques is that they can be used on a wide range of solids, liquids and gases. A disadvantage is that the 'unknown' has to be identified by comparing it to compounds already 'known'.

Comment In your revision you need to focus on at least two of the methods so that you can give the kind of detail needed to gain full marks for questions.

Q3 Medicine needs to constantly monitor various things about a patient's health, e.g. composition of the blood of patients with kidney disease and on dialysis.

Air pollution is a problem and is constantly monitored for high levels of carbon monoxide and ozone.

Comment You need to learn specific examples. In addition to the above, you could use 'quality of drinking water' and 'drug-testing of athletes'.

UNIT 14: EXAM PRACTICE
Foundation Tier (pages 138–139)

Q1 The following are mark points.

Arrhenius proposed that acids formed H^+ ions.

Arrhenius proposed that alkalis formed OH^- ions.

Brønsted and Lowry showed that H+ ions were protons.

They said that acids were *donors* of protons.

They said that alkalis were *acceptors* of protons.

(4 marks maximum, I deducted for poor English, etc.)

Examiner's Comments This question covers one of the Ideas and Evidence sections of the specifications as well as testing your ability to express chemical ideas in an extended-writing format.

You should always spend time noting down the key points you are going to cover *before* you attempt to write in your answer fully.

Remember that for questions like this there are more points worth credit than the total for the question. If you have noted down more than 4 (as you may in this question), **you should include them all in your written answer!** Before starting your answer, consider whether you should re-order your points to follow a logical pattern.

As you write your answer, try to separate different issues by starting a new paragraph for each one. In this example, Arrhenius should be in the first paragraph and Brønsted and Lowry in a second paragraph.

Q2 a Group I (1)
  b Alkali metals (1)

Examiner's Comments You are always provided with a periodic table, so finding the group 1 metals is very straightforward. Knowing the name of this family of metals should also be straighforward.

  c i) Get softer/less hard; (1) decreases/gets lower. (1)
  ii) 40 °C (1)

Examiner's Comments The table provides the data needed to answer the two questions. You need to be careful about the direction of the trend. In this case it is *down* the group. (But different questions could ask for trends going up the group.)

Rubidium is 40 °C, not 0 °C. Your guide is that the *difference* gets less down the group: Li to Na difference is 82 degrees, Na to K difference is 34 degrees, so K to Rb will be less than 34 degrees.

  d i) Diagram A (1)
  ii) Tick in last box (1)

Examiner's Comments Again, the periodic table is a guide for you since the group number tells you the number of electrons in the outer shell (1 in this case). This is why B and C are wrong in i) and why the last box in ii) is the correct response.

  e Similar reactions (1)

Examiner's Comments Elements in the same group have similar properties - one of the fundamental facts about the periodic table.

Q3 Order of substances: ammonia; ethanol; carbon; methanol; ethyl ethanoate; ethanol (6)

Examiner's Comments This question is 'recall', i.e. remembering basic chemical facts. It is quite challenging at this level since it asks for substances from many different areas of the chemistry specifications.

Your revision programme **must include learning basic information thoroughly.**

Foundation/Higher Tier overlap (pages 145–147)

Q1 a Limewater goes cloudy/milky, (1) then colourless again. (1)

Examiner's Comments This could be deduced from point 1. You should know the use of limewater as a test for carbon dioxide. Then, adding more carbon dioxide turns the insoluble calcium carbonate into soluble calcium hydrogencarbonate, so the precipitate disappears. The second mark is harder to obtain, and most 'C grade' candidates would only gain the first mark.

  b i) $CaO + CO_2$
    (both formulae needed) (1)
  ii) thermal decomposition (both terms needed) (1)

i) The answer can be deduced from the information in point 2 – a good reason for you to **read the whole of questions carefully**. Also, in a question like this where a lot of information is provided at the start, you need to **constantly** refer back to it.

ii) The answer requires both words because 'heat' is specifically mentioned in the question.

 c i) $CaO + H_2O \rightarrow Ca(OH)_2$ (correct reactant and product formula needed) (2)
  ii) Energy is given out. (1)

i) This question again highlights the need for you to keep referring back to the information at the start, since point 4 provides the information for you to answer this part.

ii) You should know that 'exo' means 'giving out'.

 d Points 1 and 3 describe carbon dioxide being removed. (1)
  Point 4 shows that the process involves recycling, so carbon dioxide continues to be removed. (1)

This part is difficult since it needs you to **summarise the overall processes involved**. The first mark should be straightforward for you to obtain, but the second mark involving the ongoing nature of the process is more difficult, and many candidates would not gain the mark.

 e The amount of carbon dioxide is increasing. (1)
  It causes the 'greenhouse effect', (1) which leads to global warming. (1)

The environmental effect of increased carbon dioxide in the atmosphere is one you should be fully aware of, and this question includes the main features of this issue.

Q2 a 'For strength' or 'Aluminium is not a very strong metal'. (either answer) (1)

A standard example of the uses of aluminium is linked to its physical properties. Aluminium is a low density (light) metal, a fact that questions often ask about.

 b Alloys have better properties than pure metals. (1)

The fact that this is only a 1-mark question should tell you that you do not need to give an *example* of a property (e.g. resistance to corrosion, stronger, etc.).

 c i) Published on article in a magazine/told others at meetings/written a book. (any two) (2)
  ii) Repeated his work and obtained the same results. (1)
  iii) Smaller/faster computers. (1)

i), ii) The way scientists publish the results of their work and check each other's results are key ideas about how scientists work.

iii) Fullerenes are not on GCSE Chemistry specifications, but this question provides all the information you need.

 d i) Carbon dioxide (1)
  ii) In a gas syringe (1)

i) The substance is pure carbon (like diamond and graphite), so the dioxide is formed when 'completely' burnt in oxygen. (Incomplete combustion would produce carbon monoxide.)

ii) 'In a tube over water' is not the best method of collecting the gas, since carbon dioxide is slightly soluble in water – a fact that is covered in other parts of the course, e.g. atmosphere and water.

Q3 a Calculations:
  A 59 kJ ÷ 6p = 9.83 kJ/p
  B 40 kJ ÷ 7p = 5.71 kJ/p
  C 42 kJ ÷ 5p = 8.40 kJ/p (1)
  Answer = A (1)

The correct working, i.e. kJ ÷ p, gains 1 mark and is essential in obtaining the correct answer, A. The commonest error is to do the wrong division (i.e. p ÷ kJ). The energy cost of fuels is one of the Ideas and Evidence sections in the specifications.

b Cleanest = B (1)

It forms no soot and leaves no solid. (1)

c Carbon monoxide (or carbon) (1) + water (1)

Higher Tier (pages 152–153)

Q1 a Less weight/mass, so cheaper to transport. (1)

b i) $1000 \text{ kg} \times 1/100 = 10 \text{ kg}$ (1)

ii) $NiO = 59 + 16 = 75$ (1)

$59 \text{ Ni} \rightarrow 75 \text{ NiO}$

$10 \text{ kg} \rightarrow 75 \times 10/59 \text{ kg}$ (1)

Max. mass $NiO = 12.7 \text{ kg}$ (1)

c Nickel is below iron in the reactivity series of metals. (1)

Carbon can remove the oxygen from nickel oxide. (1)

d i) $Ni^{2+} + 2e^- \rightarrow Ni$ (1)

ii) Any transition metal in period 6 of the periodic table, e.g. Hg (1)

Q2 a $$\text{Moles} = \frac{\text{volume (cm}^3)}{1000} \times \text{mol dm}^{-3}$$

$$= \frac{28 \times 0.5}{1000} \quad (1)$$

Number of moles $= 0.014$ (1)

b I mol NaOH reacts with 1/3 mol H_3PO4 (1)

Moles H_3PO4 = 0.014 × 1/3 = 0.0046 (1)

$$\frac{0.0046}{50} \times 1000 = 0.093 \text{ mol dm}^{-3} \text{ (1)}$$

Examiner's Comments In these types of questions where the answer from one part is used in a subsequent part, 'consequential marking' is used, i.e. you are not penalised in the second part if you use the correct method but the wrong number. This is the reason why **showing your working** is so important. If a 'list of numbers' appears without showing how they were arrived at, the candidate will lose the benefit of this 'consequential marking'. The marker will not try and work out how you arrive at the numbers!

In this question, the reaction ratio (1:1/3) is essential to achieve the expression 0.0046/50 cm^3 H$_3$PO$_4$, and the $\frac{1000}{50}$ converts the volume to 1 dm^3.

Q3 a i) Aluminium oxide (1)

Reduces the reactivity of aluminium/makes aluminium less reactive. (1)

ii) Anodising (1)

Examiner's Comments In any question on aluminium, you need always to be aware of the oxide coating (of aluminium oxide) on this metal.

b Sulphur dioxide (1)

Examiner's Comments This is the contact process, and you should recognise this from the catalyst vanadium(V) oxide. Gas Y will be sulphur trioxide.

c i) Stronger (1)

ii) Low density/light metal (1)

iii) Does not corrode/rust or less brittle (1)

Examiner's Comments You need to be fully aware of the properties of alloys as specified in the syllabus.

William Collins' dream of knowledge for all began with the publication of his first book in 1819. A self-educated mill worker, he not only enriched millions of lives, but also founded a flourishing publishing house. Today, staying true to this spirit, Collins books are packed with inspiration, innovation and practical expertise. They place you at the centre of a world of possibility and give you exactly what you need to explore it.

Collins. Do more.

Published by Collins
An imprint of HarperCollins*Publishers*
77-85 Fulham Palace Road
London W6 8JB

Browse the complete Collins catalogue at
www.collinseducation.com

© HarperCollins*Publishers* Limited 2005

First published 2005

10 9 8 7 6 5 4 3 2 1

ISBN 0 00 719057 3

Sam Goodman and Chris Sunley assert their moral rights to be identified as the authors of this work.

British Library Cataloguing in Publication Data
A catalogue record for this publication is available from the British Library.

Acknowledgements
The Authors and Publisher are grateful to the following for permission to reproduce copyright material:
AQA: pp. 136, 138 (Q1), 140, 141, 147, 151, 153, (Q2)
Edexcel: pp. 137, 139 (Q3), 144, 146, 150, 153 (Q3)
OCR: pp.135, 138 (Q2), 142, 145, 148, 152

Photographs
Corbis 19 (upper), 86 (upper); Corbis/Angela Hornak 86 (lower); GeoScience Features 71 (left); Andrew Lambert 19 (lower), 72, 105 (left, centre, right); Alfred Pasieka 14 (upper); Science Photo Library: Andrew Lambert 37, 71 (right), Andrew McClenaghan 14 (lower), Lawrence Migdale 20, Cordelia Molloy 110, Sheila Terry 121, Geoff Tompkinson 132, 133.

Illustrations
Roger Bastow, Harvey Collins, Richard Deverell, Jerry Fowler, Gecko Ltd, Ian Law, Mike Parsons, Dave Poole, Chris Rothero and Tony Warne

Every effort has been made to contact the holders of copyright material, but if any have been inadvertently overlooked, the Publishers will be pleased to make the necessary arrangements at the first opportunity.

Edited by Pat Winter
Series and book design by Sally Boothroyd
Index compiled by Ann Lloyd Griffiths
Production by Katie Butler
Printed and bound by Printing Express, Hong Kong

You might also like to visit
www.harpercollins.co.uk
The book lover's website